Do You Remember?

THE 1950s

An exclusive edition for

ALLSORTED.
for all your gift books and gift stationery

Watford, Herts, U.K. WD19 4BG

ALLSORTED.

for all your gift books and gift stationery

Published in 2016 by Allsorted. Watford, Herts, U.K. WD19 4BG

Compiled by Michael Powell
Illustrations reproduced courtesy of Shutterstock.com
Concept by Milestone Design
Designed by Joanna Ross at Double Fish Design Ltd

Printed in China

*Every effort has been made to ensure the accuracy of the information contained in this book.
In the unlikely case of queries please contact the compilers via their website www.susannageoghegan.com.*

Contents

THE YEAR THAT WAS

1950

1. On 31st January, President Harry S. Truman ordered the development of what, following the first Soviet test-detonation of an atomic bomb the previous year?

2. Why was Hollywood icon Ingrid Bergman the focus of much negative press attention from 2nd February?

3. On 9th February, Senator Joseph McCarthy made an inflammatory speech in which he accused the US Senate of being filled with 205 what?

4. Which Disney movie premiered in Boston on 15th February?

5. Who became British Prime Minister following the General Election on 23rd February?

6. On 22nd March, what demand did Egypt make of the British government?

7. On 23rd March, the 5 Best Picture nominees at the 22nd Academy Awards shared one thing in common. What was it?

8. Which iconic British comic was first released on 14th April?

9. On 27th April, South Africa passed the Group Areas Act. What did this do?

10. On 6th May, what was unearthed by archaeologists in the Jutland Peninsula, Denmark?

11. On 9th May, a former science-fiction writer published a book that founded a global religion. What was the title?

12. On 29th May, BBC Light Programme aired a pilot episode of which long-running radio programme?

13. On 27th June, President Harry S. Truman ordered the involvement of US troops in which conflict?

14. On 16th July, which South American nation won the World Cup?

15. On 8th August, which American woman set a new record for swimming the English Channel from France to England?

16. On 23rd August, which legendary African-American singer and actor tried and failed to get his US passport reinstated after having been accused of Communist sympathies?

17. On 30th September, President Harry S. Truman's National Security Council Report 68 (NCS-68) set in stone what US foreign policy objective?

18. On 2nd October, which iconic comic strip made its debut appearance in seven US newspapers?

19. On 13th October, which of James Stewart's classic movies premiered in the US?

20. On 22nd November, which former child starlet retired from showbiz?

THE YEAR THAT WAS

1951

1. Which long-running British radio series aired for the first time on 1st January?

2. On 27th January, what military operation began at a site in Nevada, US, 65 miles from Las Vegas?

3. On 27th February, the 22nd Amendment to the US Constitution was ratified. What did it specify?

4. On 29th March, which Rogers and Hammerstein musical premiered on Broadway, making a new star of a young actor named Yul Brynner?

5. On 29th March, *All About Eve* was named Best Picture at the 23rd Annual Academy Awards. Who were the film's two female leads?

6. A stone slab, used for centuries in the coronation of Scottish monarchs, reappeared on the altar of Arbroath Abbey on 11th April, months after disappearing from Westminster Abbey. What was it called?

7. On 12th April, which country formed its inaugural Olympic Committee, ahead of competing for the first time in 1952?

8. Which cultural centre was opened by King George VI on London's Southbank on 3rd May?

9. Which rousing national exhibition opened on 3rd May?

10. Which iconic British comedy series debuted on the BBC Home Service on 28th May?

11. Bass-Baritone, William Warfield, achieved overnight fame following the premiere of which classic Hollywood musical in New York on 13th July?

12. Which British musical, directed by David Lean, was screened in the US on 30th July, only after several minutes of allegedly anti-Semitic footage was cut?

13. Which classic of American literature was first published on 12th August?

14. Which all-female competition was held for the first time on 15th August, as part of the Festival of Britain celebrations?

15. On 20th September, which two European nations were accepted into NATO?

16. On 26th September, what three-day weather phenomenon could be seen over Europe, as a result of Canadian forest fires?

17. Following a General Election on 26th October, who took over as British Prime Minister?

18. What common road safety feature was first introduced in the UK on 31st October?

19. On 3rd November, the first British supermarket chain opened its inaugural branch in Streatham, London. What was it called?

20. Which Hollywood classic, starring Humphrey Bogart and Katharine Hepburn, premiered in the US on 23rd December?

THE YEAR THAT WAS

1952

1. On 16th January, what programme debuted on the BBC that would become the country's longest-running television show for children?

2. On 1st February, what appeared on British streets for the first time, in an effort to combat widespread failure to purchase a television licence?

3. On 6th February, why did Princess Elizabeth cut short her official visit to Kenya and fly home?

4. On 21st February, what wartime hangover was finally abolished in the UK?

5. On 20th March, the US finally ratified a peace treaty with which country?

6. On 7th April, which US television show was declared the first to have been watched in ten million households?

7. On 15th April, which US military aircraft flew for the first time?

8. On 29th April, which British city became the first to establish a new university since the War?

9. On 3rd May, which British football team won the FA Cup for an historic fifth time?

10. Which French Nobel Prize-winning author had his books added to the Catholic Church's 'Index of Forbidden Books' on 1st June?

11. Whose diary was published on 15th June?

12. On 15th July, crowds gathered on London streets to bid farewell to what?

13. On 19th July, the Summer Olympics opened in which city?

14. On 16th August, storms of tropical intensity hit the South of England hard. Which Exmoor town was especially badly hit?

15. What did an American composer do on stage at Woodstock on 29th August for 4 minutes and 33 seconds?

16. Which English-born Hollywood star, en route to the UK on 19th September, was told he would be refused re-entry to the US on the grounds of his political beliefs?

17. What appeared on the front page of the *Manchester Guardian* for the first time in its history on 29th September?

18. Why did a 15-year-old boy from Newthorpe, Nottinghamshire, named Jack Bamford, hit the headlines in the UK on 19th October?

19. Who won the US Presidential election on 4th November?

20. Which long-running play first opened in London's West End on 25th November?

THE YEAR THAT WAS

1953

1. What play, by an Irish playwright, received its debut on a stage in Paris on 5th January?

2. On 13th January, which profession did Soviet newspaper *Pravda* allege was conspiring against Soviet military and political leadership?

3. On 5th February, what gave the children of the UK cause for celebration?

4. Which Disney movie premiered in the US on 5th February?

5. What scientific discovery did American microbiologist James D. Watson and British microbiologist Francis Crick announce on 28th February?

6. Why did a modest flat at 10, Rillington Place, in London's Notting Hill become headline news from 24th March?

7. Which royal funeral took place at Windsor on 31st March?

8. Which literary legend made his first appearance in a novel published on 13th April?

9. Which British icon was knighted by Queen Elizabeth on 24th April?

10. Which two mountaineers became the first to reach the summit of Mount Everest on 29th May?

11. Which royal event took place on 2nd June?

12. What did Sidney Gottleib approve for use by CIA personnel in the top secret Project MKUltra on 9th June?

13. Which iconic British science-fiction television series first aired on 18th July?

14. What nostalgic British musical television series made its debut on 20th July?

15. Which Marilyn Monroe movie premiered in the US on 23rd July?

16. Which captain helped England win the Ashes for the first time in 19 years on 19th August?

17. Which iconic US political figure married at St Mary's Roman Catholic Church, Newport, Rhode Island on 12th September?

18. On 6th October, which global aid fund was made a permanent specialised United Nations agency?

19. On 21st November, what did paleoanthropologists at the British National History Museum denounce as a hoax?

20. What household product went on sale for the first time on 30th December, in the US?

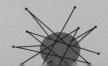

THE YEAR THAT WAS

1954

1. Who did American baseball player, Joe DiMaggio, marry on 14th January?

2. Which famed British poet's radio play was aired posthumously for the first time on 25th January, two months after his death in New York?

3. At a press conference in London on 12th February, what did the British Medical Council and Health Minister Iain MacLeod confirm for the first time could cause cancer?

4. Which vaccination programme was rolled out for the first time to children in the US on 23rd February?

5. In the US on 1st March, the government announced that a hydrogen bomb had been tested in which coral reef ring in the Pacific Ocean?

6. On 25th March, which movie, starring Deborah Kerr, Donna Reid, Burt Lancaster, Frank Sinatra and Montgomery Clift, won 8 Oscars at the 26th Annual Academy Awards?

7. On 4th April, at the Carnegie Hall, which legendary Italian symphonic conductor famously suffered a minor lapse of memory, prompting programmers to panic and take the broadcast off air?

8. Which passenger jet airliner was rolled out into general production on 14th May?

9. In Birmingham on 29th May, who became the first woman to run a mile in under five minutes?

10. Which epic work of literature was first published on 6th June?

11. Which computer scientist and wartime Bletchley Park code-breaker ended his life on 7th June?

12. Which sporting body was formed in Basel, Switzerland on 15th June?

13. On 30th June, what was witnessed in the skies over Britain for the first time since 1927?

14. What officially came off-ration in the UK for the first time on 4th July?

15. Which Himalayan peak was first conquered on 31st July by Italian mountaineers, Lino Lacedelli and Achille Compagnoni?

16. Which sporting magazine first appeared on the shelves in the US on 16th August?

17. On 3rd September, the final episode of a 21-year-old radio series, much loved by children on both sides of the pond, aired in the US. What was it?

18. On 19th October, Britain agreed to end its military occupation of which region?

19. On 2nd November, which radio comedy series debuted on BBC radio, focussing on the life of a down-at-heel comedian in his home at 23, Railway Cuttings?

20. On 4th December, a new restaurant opened its doors for the first time in Miami, Florida. It would grow to become a global phenomenon. What was it?

THE YEAR THAT WAS

1955

1. On 7th January, the first British-made full-length animated feature film went on general release. What was it?

2. What caused havoc around the UK on 24th February, forcing the Royal Air Force to intervene in some regions?

3. Who made his television debut on 5th March in a US television programme called *Louisiana Hayride?*

4. What musical number had teenagers dancing in the aisles of the movie theatres when the movie *Blackboard Jungle* premiered in the US on 20th March?

5. On 29th March, which British trade union declared a strike that would continue until 14th June, prompting a state of emergency to be declared?

6. In what country did the EOKA begin a terrorist campaign against British rule on 1st April?

7. On 6th April, following the resignation of Sir Winston Churchill the previous day due to ill health, who took over as British Prime Minister?

8. On 15th April, in Des Plaines, Illinois, American businessman, Ray Kroc, opened the first of what would become a global restaurant chain. What was it called?

9. On 18th April, whose death prompted President Eisenhower to say, 'no other man was more modest in the possession of the power that is knowledge'?

10. Which big screen wartime classic, starring Michael Redgrave, was released in the UK on 16th May?

11. What did the Children and Young Persons' Act protect children from in the UK from 6th June?

12. What landmark in British legal history took place at Holloway Prison on 13th July?

13. What iconic site opened in Anaheim, California on 17th July?

14. Which Disney movie was released in the UK on 16th August?

15. What book hit the shelves in the UK for the first time on 17th August and went on to set a record as the best-selling copyrighted book of all time?

16. On 4th September, which two men made history as the first newsreaders ever to read a television news bulletin in the UK?

17. On 24th September, President Dwight D. Eisenhower suffered a coronary thrombosis, forcing which Vice President to step into the Oval Office?

18. On 23rd October, which British intelligence officer was named 'The Third Man' in the infamous Cambridge Spy Ring?

19. On 19th November, in a satirical article in *The Economist*, which naval historian lent his name to a law stipulating that, 'work expands so as to fill the time available for its completion'?

20. The movie adaptation of which Shakespeare play, starring Laurence Olivier, premiered in London on 13th December?

THE YEAR THAT WAS

1956

1. In which country did the Winter Olympics open on 26th January?

2. What iconic public transport first went into service in London on 8th February?

3. On 22nd February, which track put Elvis Presley into the US music charts for the first time since signing with record label, RCA Victor?

4. Which song did Doris Day record on 24th February as part of the soundtrack for Hitchcock's *The Man Who Knew Too Much*?

5. A memorial to which political figure was unveiled at London's Highgate Cemetery on 14th March, by the General Secretary of the Communist Party of Great Britain?

6. Which country became the world's first Islamist Republic on 23rd March?

7. Which British football club won the First Division League title on 7th April, with players averaging just 24 years of age?

8. In his Budget Speech of 17th April, what did Chancellor Harold

Macmillan announce would go on sale from 1st November in the UK?

9. Which Hollywood icon's wedding made world news on 19th April?

10. Which heavyweight boxing champion retired on 27th April, without ever having lost a professional boxing match?

11. What public health campaign did Health Minister Robin Turton refuse to launch on 7th May, arguing that there was as yet inadequate medical evidence?

12. In which 'angry young man's' play at the Royal Court did a young Alan Bates first make a name for himself on 8th May?

13. Which annual international contest took place for the first time on 24th May in Switzerland?

14. Why was Third Class travel scrapped on British Railways trains from 3rd June?

15. Why were television viewers of *The Milton Berle Show* in the US scandalised on 5th June?

16. On 28th June, a bill introduced by MP Sydney Silverman passed in the House of Commons. What did the bill seek to abolish?

17. Which Hollywood comedy duo performed their act together for the last time at Copacabana, New York on 24th July?

18. Which iconic British restaurant chain opened its first store in Bristol on 27th July?

19. What wartime bomber, famed as the plane that carried Barnes Wallis' Bouncing Bomb, was retired from service in the RAF on 15th October?

20. On 25th December, which classic television advertising campaign made its debut, featuring anthropomorphised animals?

THE YEAR THAT WAS

1957

1. What was notable about the new watch introduced on 3rd January by the Hamilton Watch Company?

2. How did South African cricketer Russell Endean make cricketing history on 5th January?

3. Who was described by Ed Sullivan as 'thoroughly all right' on the occasion of his appearance on *The Ed Sullivan Show* on 6th January, despite only being partially shown on screen?

4. Who took over as Prime Minister of Great Britain on 10th January, following the resignation of Anthony Eden the previous day?

5. What much-loved plastic recreational sporting item first hit the shelves in the US on 13th January?

6. What was the Toddlers' Truce, abolished in the UK on 16th February?

7. Which much-loved and enduring rhyming children's book was released in the US on 1st March?

8. What report on the BBC's *Panorama* was the first known aired April Fool's Day Hoax, on 1st April?

9. On 24th April, the BBC aired the first episode of an astronomy programme that would run with the same presenter until his death in December 2012. What was the programme and who was the presenter?

10. What accidentally fell from a US Air Force bomber near Albuquerque on 22nd May?

11. Which British football legend played his last international soccer game on 15th May, ending a record 23-year career?

12. Which two teenagers met for the first time at a garden fete at St Peter's Church in Woolton, Liverpool on 6th July, beginning a partnership that would change British pop music?

13. Which British driver became the first to win a World Championship title at the British Grand Prix at Aintree on 20th July?

14. What did Harold Macmillan tell a gathering of the British Conservative Party on 20th July?

15. Which classic British cartoon character made its debut in the *Daily Mirror* on 5th August?

16. When the Wolfenden Report was published on 4th September, what change to British law did it recommend?

17. Which British observatory became operational from 11th October?

18. On 3rd November, the Soviet Union sent *Sputnik 2* into orbit. Who was inside?

19. Which British province received a dedicated Minister of State at Westminster for the first time on 12th December?

20. What happened on 25th December for the first time in British history?

THE YEAR THAT WAS

1958

1. Which Soviet satellite fell out of orbit and down to Earth on 4th January?

2. Which sporting tragedy took place in Munich on 6th February?

3. Which campaign was launched in the UK by Bertrand Russell on 25th February?

4. London gained an all-new tourist attraction on 21st March. What was it?

5. Which star was inducted into the US Army for military service on 24th March?

6. Work began in the UK on 24th March on which motorway?

7. Who became Soviet Premier on 27th March?

8. What received a moral green light from the Church of England on 7th April?

9. Who were allowed to sit in the House of Lords for the first time following the Life Peerages Act of 30th April?

10. Which Hollywood musical, directed by Vincent Minnelli and starring Maurice Chevalier, opened in New York on 15th May?

11. What award was presented at Buckingham Palace on 4th June for the first time?

12. Which wartime submarine technology was the subject of an article in *The Lancet* on 7th June, in which its medical diagnostic applications were discussed?

13. What were installed on British streets for the first time on 10th July?

14. Which title was bestowed upon Prince Charles by the Queen on 26th July?

15. Which scientific agency was first created by US Congress on 29th July?

16. On 1st August, the first in what would become a series of British comedy *Carry On* movies premiered in the UK. What was it called?

17. Which pop song, released on 29th August, has been credited as the first British rock 'n' roll track?

18. Which war broke out between Britain and Iceland on 1st September?

19. Which long-running British children's TV programme first aired on 16th October?

20. What were exhibited at Earl's Court on 24th November, the first time they had been exhibited anywhere in the world?

THE YEAR THAT WAS

1959

1. Who took control of Cuba from 6th January?

2. Who was sworn in as President of France on 8th January?

3. Which record company was founded in Detroit by Berry Gordy, Jr. on 12th January?

4. Which Disney movie was released in the US on 29th January, the first to feature a stereophonic soundtrack?

5. Which nation gained independence from the UK on 19th February?

6. Which hapless band of brothers made their final television appearance in the US on 8th March?

7. Which iconic toy hit the market on 9th March, sporting a fashionable high ponytail, a striped one-piece bathing suit and heels?

8. Who were the Mercury Seven, announced on 9th April?

9. Which British dancer was released from prison in Panama on 22nd April?

10. On which brand new music programme did Pete Murray, Alma Cogan, Gary Miller and Susan Stranks feature on 1st June?

11. In which movie, released on 18th June, did Audrey Hepburn star in what she would later describe as her favourite role?

12. Which Manhattan Project spy was released and allowed to leave the US and return to Germany on 23rd June?

13. What experiment did the Royal Mail introduce in Norwich on 28th July?

14. Which was the first British bank to use a computer, on 4th August?

15. Which iconic British car went on sale for the first time on 26th August?

16. On 4th September, what was the first man-made object ever to crash land on the surface of the Moon?

17. What invention was released on the market for the first time on 16th September, changing life for office workers forever?

18. Which political party won the British General Election on 8th October?

19. On 17th November, what became available at Prestwick and Renfrew Airports for the first time anywhere in the UK?

20. Which popular British transport-themed children's television programme aired for the first time on 28th December?

ADVERTISING
SLOGANS
OF THE FIFTIES

keep your teeth clean

1. Name the product, 1955:
   'It's so big, you've got to grin to get it in'

2. Complete the slogan, 1955:
   'Someone isn't using . . .'

3. Name the product, 1955:
   'The tingling fresh toothpaste for teeth and gums'

4. Complete the slogan, 1955:
'. . . too good to hurry'

5. Name the product, 1956:
'Tea you can really taste'

6. Complete the slogan, 1956:
'Don't say brown, say . . .'

7. Name the product, 1956:
'When only the best will do'

8. Complete the slogan, 1957:
'Make friends with a . . .'

9. Complete the slogan, 1957:
'. . .gives a meal man appeal'

10. Name the product, 1957:
'You can't have too much'

11. Complete the slogan, 1957:
'Start your day the . . .'

12. Name the product, 1957:
'The key to comfort'

13. Complete the slogan, 1957:
'Top people take . . .'

14. Name the product, 1957:
'The sign of a good bread'

15. Name the product, 1958:
'Adds brightness to whiteness'

16. Complete the slogan, 1958:
'Don't forget the . . .'

17. Complete the slogan, 1958:
'I told 'em . . .'

18. Name the product, 1958:
'Full of Eastern promise'

19. Name the product, 1959:
'So much more than a toy'

20. Complete the slogan, 1959:
'Whoever minds how he dines
demands . . .'

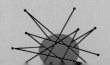

AN ECLECTIC MIX OF

Human Advances

1. In 1950, the last in the first wave of New Towns built across the UK to cope with the post-war housing crisis, was designated. Where in the East Midlands was it?

2. In 1950, a Frenchman named Marcel Bich launched a brand new pen onto the European market. By which name would it become known?

3. In 1952, an American design company released the Seeburg M100C onto the market, the first 100-play model of what culturally iconic apparatus?

4. In December 1952, which remarkable weather phenomenon descended on the Greater London area, causing cows to choke?

5. In 1953, an Englishman and a Nepalese-born Indian made global headlines for which remarkable feat?

6. In 1953, the US Supreme Court made an historic ruling, bringing electoral equality into force across all US states for the first time. What was it?

7. In 1954, another US Supreme Court ruling took the country a step closer to racial equality. What was it?

8. In 1954, the British newspaper,

the *Daily Mail* funded the first official Himalayan expedition to search for which elusive cryptid?

9. In 1954, a junior doctor achieved which landmark sporting record at the Iffley Road track at Oxford University?

10. On 1st December, 1955, a riot broke out in Montgomery, Alabama over which incident on a public bus?

11. In 1955, a British engineer named Peter Hobbs invented the first automatic version of a particular kitchen appliance. What was it?

12. In 1955, an American animator opened an innovative family resort in California. What was it?

13. In 1956, which heavyweight boxer became the first to retire undefeated across all 49 of his professional fights?

14. In 1957, the Soviets launched the first man-made object into space. What was it?

15. In 1957, why did a stray dog rescued from the streets of Moscow make international news?

16. In 1958, how did Bobby Fischer, a 15-year-old boy from St Louis, Missouri, make history?

17. In 1958, a British designer named Gerald Holtom incorporated two semaphore letters into a new logo for a protest march in London. The logo would beame iconic. What was it?

18. In 1958, a national British charity launched its round-the-clock home-nursing service for cancer patients. What was the charity?

19. In 1959, 12 nations signed a treaty in Washington pledging to establish which of the Earth's continents as a scientific preserve, free from any military activity?

20. In 1959, Spanish track and field athlete, Miguel de la Quadra-Salcedo, set a new and controversial world record using a revolutionary new technique in which competitive field event?

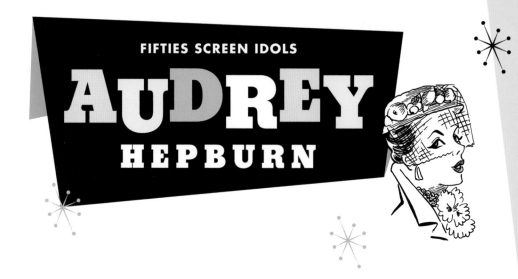

FIFTIES SCREEN IDOLS
AUDREY HEPBURN

1. Where did Audrey Hepburn spend her childhood years?

2. Her childhood experience of famine in the Netherlands under Nazi occupation led Hepburn to devote a great deal of her life to humanitarian efforts with which international children's organisation?

3. True or False: Hepburn was fluent in five languages.

4. While Hepburn was on the set of a small French-English movie in 1951, novelist Colette cast her on the spot in the title role in which stage musical?

5. Which 1953 Hollywood movie saw Hepburn play her first big screen lead?

6. In which 1953 movie does Hepburn declare, 'I've never been alone with a man before, even with my dress on. With my dress off, it's *most* unusual'.

7. In 1955, Hepburn married the Hollywood actor whom she would

star opposite in *War and Peace.* Who was he?

8. In which 1957 musical comedy did Hepburn star as a beatnik bookstore clerk?

9. In which 1957 movie does Hepburn's character describe Americans as 'immunized, mechanized, air-conditioned and hydromatic'?

10. In which 1959 movie did Hepburn play Sister Luke?

11. Which movie role did Hepburn decline in 1959, on the grounds that it would stir too many painful memories of her war years in occupied Holland?

12. Hepburn joined the set of which iconic movie a few months after the birth of her son, Sean, in 1960?

13. In which 1960 movie about a family living on the Frontier did Hepburn break her back in a fall from a horse?

14. Which role did Hepburn describe as 'the hardest thing I ever did', because it demanded that she portray an extrovert?

15. Which British big screen heart-throb famously said, 'All I want for Christmas is another picture with Audrey Hepburn'?

16. To which song was Henry Mancini referring when he said, 'There have been more than a thousand versions. . .but hers was unquestionably the greatest'?

17. What did Hepburn describe as 'always a good idea'?

18. How did Hepburn say she preferred to 'refuel'?

19. Which of her features did Hepburn once confess to feeling embarrassed by?

20. What was auctioned off in December 2006 to raise almost half a million pounds for a children's charity in India?

1950 TO 1953

SPORTING EVENTS

1. Where did the 1950 Football World Cup take place?

2. Who won the 1950 World Heavyweight Championship over 15 rounds in New York?

3. Which South African golfer won the British Open in 1950?

4. In Formula One, which event took place for the first time at Silverstone?

5. Which team won the 1950 Oxford vs Cambridge boat race?

6. Who won the Women's singles title at Wimbledon in 1950?

7. Who won the FA Cup in 1951?

8. Who defeated Sugar Ray Robinson in 1951 to take the middleweight boxing championship title?

9. Which American golfer won the Masters and the US Open golf tournaments in 1951?

10. Which Argentine Formula One driver, known as 'El Maestro', won the World Drivers' Championship in 1951?

11. Which nation won the Five Nations Rugby Union championship in 1951?

12. Which American tennis player defeated Australian Ken McGregor at the Australian Open and at Wimbledon in 1951?

13. Which team topped the FA First Division in 1952?

14. In 1952 at the Yankee Stadium, American boxer Sugar Ray Robinson failed to win back his world light heavyweight title against Joey Maxim and, in the process, suffered what for the only time in his professional career?

15. Who won the World Heavyweight Championship title in 1952?

16. What sport was founded in the US in 1952 by promoters Jess McMahon and Toots Mondt?

17. Who won the FA Cup in 1953, known as the Matthews Final because of the performance of winger, Stanley Matthews?

18. Which British partnership won the ice dancing championship title at the World Figure Skating Championships in 1953?

19. Which nation won the Five Nations Championship in 1953?

20. Who won the World Snooker Championship in 1953?

BRITISH
TELEVISION
IN THE 1950s

1. Jack Warner starred as which iconic police constable from 1955 until 1976?

2. What was the first British television programme designed specifically for preschoolers, which first aired in 1953?

3. Which current affairs programme first aired in 1953 and would become the longest-running of its genre in the world?

4. Which quiz show, hosted by Hughie Green, transferred from Radio Luxembourg to ITV, days after the channel launched?

5. Which soap opera was set in the Oxbridge General Hospital?

6. Which talent show transferred to ITV from Radio Luxembourg in June 1956?

7. Which weekly variety show debuted in 1955 and was first hosted by Tommy Trinder?

8. Which BBC sports programme was hosted by David Coleman from its fourth episode in 1958?

9. Which children's television programme featured a puppet named Mr Turnip, who was fond of declaring, 'Lawky, lawky, lum'?

10. What series, based on real memoirs of a Scotland Yard detective, was the first police crime drama in British television history?

11. Which 1956 pirate drama series was partially filmed on a real schooner off the coast of Falmouth, Cornwall?

12. Which farming family of marionettes appeared on *Watch With Mother* from 1955?

13. In 1958, what programme focused entirely on music with a target audience of teenagers, the first of its kind in the UK?

14. From 1955, which biographical television programme opened each week with a different celebrity guest being surprised with a Big Red Book?

15. Which craft was the subject of the most famous of the BBC's early Interlude films, designed to fill the frequent breakdowns in transmission?

16. What product was the focus of the first ever British television commercial in 1955, with the jingle, 'It's tingling fresh. It's fresh as ice'?

17. At the end of the first commercial break, an advert for Watney's beer urged viewers, 'You try it'. What was the next thing viewers saw when the programme returned?

18. In 1955, Cliff Adams and the Stargazers appeared on *Sunday Night at the London Palladium* dressed as Guardsmen in bearskins, just three months after performing the jingle for what television commercial?

19. Cliff Adams released another record, 'The Lonely Man Theme', prompted by the success of a jingle he wrote for which other television commercial in 1959?

20. Advertisers on the first British television commercials were only permitted to retain a percentage of the revenue. What happened to the rest?

CLASSIC FIFTIES

MOVIES

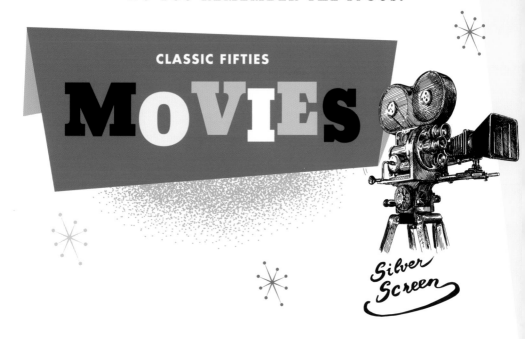

Silver Screen

1. Which 1950 film noir movie starred Gloria Swanson as a faded star of the Silent Era?

2. Which 1950 Western saw John Wayne take on the Apaches as Union Officer Kirby Yorke?

3. Which 1951 epic Roman love story starred Robert Taylor and Deborah Kerr, and saw Peter Ustinov play Nero?

4. Which Vincent Minnelli musical saw Gene Kelly fall in love with an already spoken-for Leslie Caron in 1951?

5. Which 1952 iconic Hollywood musical followed the plight of a silent movie production company struggling to make the transition to talkies?

6. Which Tennessee Williams stage classic was adapted for the big screen in 1952, starring Marlon Brando and Vivien Leigh?

7. Which 1953 Hollywood musical saw Doris Day swoon over Howard Keel's Wild Bill Hickok?

8. Which 1953 rom-com saw Marilyn Monroe, Betty Grable and Lauren Bacall set out to find love and diamonds?

9. Which 1954 thriller focused on the adventures of a wheelchair-bound nosey neighbour?

10. What did Rosemary Clooney, Danny Kaye and Bing Crosby come together to dream of in 1954?

11. Which Hollywood musical starred Frank Sinatra, Marlon Brando and Jean Simmons in 1955?

12. Which 1955 Hitchcock movie starred Grace Kelly and Cary Grant?

13. In which 1956 movie did Grace Kelly make her last screen appearance before becoming Princess Grace of Monaco?

14. Which 1956 movie saw Yul Brynner give an Oscar-winning performance in a role he performed on stage 4,625 times?

15. Which 1957 movie left dog-lovers in tears?

16. Which 1957 Western saw Burt Lancaster and Kirk Douglas re-enacting a legendary encounter between Marshall Wyatt Earp and outlaw Doc Holliday?

17. Which 1958 classic gothic horror brought together the kings of the genre, Vincent Price and Peter Cushing?

18. Which 1958 futuristic sci-fi horror brought Vincent Price back to the big screen?

19. Which 1959 Billy Wilder comedy starred Marilyn Monroe, and saw Tony Curtis and Jack Lemmon drag-up in order to flee from the Mob?

20. Which 1959 epic saw Charlton Heston sold into slavery?

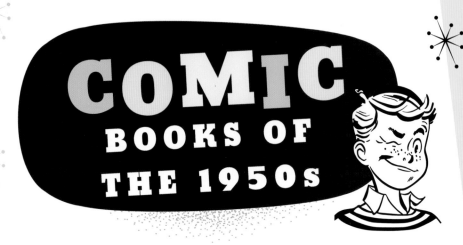

COMIC BOOKS OF THE 1950s

1. Which popular pre-war British comic for children endured into and beyond the start of the 1950s, selling almost two million copies every week by 1950?

2. Which pre-war comic dropped the word 'Comic' from its title and reverted back to weekly issues in 1950?

3. Which working-class grafter, a champion runner, appeared in *The Rover* throughout the 1950s, often scuppered in his efforts by the skullduggery of rich boys?

4. *The Rover* also featured a prose adventure story about a Second World War working-class bomber pilot who refused to accept promotion beyond the rank of Sergeant. Who was he?

5. Which comic was launched in the UK in 1950 by an Anglican priest, with a groundbreaking format in which action stories were combined with cartoon strips and a higher quality of artwork and printing?

6. Which character was featured in a coloured strip on the front cover of that same comic?

7. Which children's television character featured on the front cover of TV Comic every week from its first publication in 1951 until 1955?

8. In May 1952, what comics did the British newspaper, *The People's Post* suggest should be banned?

9. How did US comic *Tales From the Crypt* first arrive in the UK in the early 1950s?

10. In 1955, what was the consequence on the comic book industry of a pressure campaign that had included the Archbishop of Canterbury and the National Union of Teachers?

11. Which chore- and homework-avoiding character first appeared in *The Beano* in 1953?

12. Which comic first launched in 1953, with 'Mickey the Monkey' as the front cover strip each week?

13. Which British comic ceased publication in 1953 after 63 years in print, but was mentioned in Clive Dunn's 1971 hit song, 'Grandad'?

14. Which 1954 comic focused largely on sporting stories?

15. Which fictional footballing hero made his debut in the same comic in 1954, proving so popular, he earned his own comic in 1976?

16. The British comic *Knockout* featured weekly adventure stories about a fictional American cowboy from 1954. Who was he?

17. In January 1956, a new British comic was published in tabloid format, making it twice the size of most other comics. What was it?

18. In which British comic did the strip, 'Jet-Ace Logan' first appear in 1956, telling of the interplanetary adventures of an RAF pilot in 2056?

19. Which story paper (which ran with prose stories rather than comic strips) ran until 1959 with adventures from a fictional boarding school, The Red Circle School, before converting to comic book format in 1959?

20. Which fictional schoolboy made appearances throughout the 1950s in the comic book, *Knockout*, having been drawn from his pre-war appearances in the prose story paper, *The Magnet*?

FIFTIES SCREEN IDOLS

ELIZABETH
TAYLOR

1. What was Taylor's nationality?

2. Which 1944 movie about a young girl who wins a thoroughbred horse in a raffle launched 12-year-old Taylor as one of Hollywood's hottest teen actors?

3. Which event in Taylor's personal life in 1950 was organised by MGM studios as part of their promotion for her upcoming movie, *Father of the Bride*?

4. In which 1951 epic did Elizabeth Taylor and Sophia Loren appear as supporting artists?

5. In which 1954 F. Scott Fitzgerald adaptation, set in Paris, did Taylor star along with Walter Pidgeon, Donna Reed and Eva Gabor?

6. Whose death in 1955 reportedly sent Taylor into a psychiatric hospital for several days?

7. In which 1956 movie did Taylor play Carroll Baker's mother, an actress 9 months Taylor's senior?

8. Which Hollywood leading man crashed his car into a tree after leaving a party at Elizabeth Taylor's house in 1956?

9. In which 1956 movie does Elizabeth Taylor say, 'Money isn't everything, Jett'?

10. Which movie was she two weeks into filming in March 1958 when her husband, producer Mike Todd, was killed in a plane crash?

11. After Taylor's high-profile extra-marital affair with Eddie Fisher in 1959, MGM capitalised on her reputation as a homewrecker by casting her as a prostitute in which movie?

12. In which 1959 movie did Taylor give a Golden Globe-winning performance as Catherine, a traumatised woman whose family want her lobotomised?

13. How many men did Elizabeth Taylor marry?

14. Who did Elizabeth Taylor say had been among her best leading men?

15. What do 'big girls' need, according to Elizabeth Taylor?

16. To which theatrical character, from a 1939 Brecht play, did Taylor famously compare herself?

17. Taylor was raised a Christian Scientist, but in 1959 converted to which religion?

18. In which 1959 movie does Elizabeth Taylor say, 'Cut the truth out of my brain, is that what you want, Aunt Vi?'

19. In which 1960 movie does Taylor drive (and crash) a red Sunbeam Alpine?

20. Elizabeth Taylor was the first woman to earn $1 million from a movie. Which movie?

FASHION
IN THE FIFTIES

1. Whose 'New Look', unveiled in 1947, came to define the female silhouette throughout the 1950s?

2. Which influential British designer fashioned the dress Queen Elizabeth II wore for her coronation in June 1953?

3. Alfred Hitchcock's 1955 movie, *To Catch a Thief*, saw Grace Kelly sport the world's first 'IT' bag, later named in Kelly's honour. Who designed it?

4. What style of dress, first popularised by Carroll Baker in her 1956 movie of the same name, was made chic by Spanish designer, Cristóbal Balenciaga?

5. Which musical icon set the tone for young men's fashion from 1956, with his slicked-up hair, high-waisted trousers and a rockabilly, biker chic look?

6. Which French fashion house, founded in 1952, was launched to global renown thanks to the designer's partnership with Hollywood icon, Audrey Hepburn?

7. Which High Street ready-to-wear chain store appeared in cities across the UK, doubling its profits over the course of the decade?

8. Whose 1957 'sack' dress collection caught the eye of London designer Mary Quant, who developed the mini shift dress in the 1960s?

9. Which crease-proof polyester fabric was introduced in the 1950s high-end stores but soon became widely sought after?

10. The women of Britain headed into hair salons for the permanent waved hair sported by which two British icons of the decade?

11. What lingerie design trend was popularised by 'Sweater Girl', Lana Turner?

12. The cosmetics brand label, Max Factor, brought out an alternative to its popular Pan Cake in 1953, the first to combine a base and a powder. What was it called?

13. Which cosmetics company sent its cosmetics reps door-to-door in the UK for the first time in the 1950s?

14. What name was commonly given to a popular hairstyle in the early years of the decade, popularised by Italian actresses such as Gina Lollobrigida and Sophia Loren?

15. Which hairstyle, popular with teenagers, was sported by the early version of the Barbie doll?

16. Why did cosmetic scientists add titanium to cosmetics during the decade?

17. What was the name given to the thick crepe-soled, suede shoes favoured by Teddy Boys?

18. What stylish animal icon was appliqued onto full skirts by designer Juli Charlot at the start of the decade, becoming an instant hit with teenagers?

19. By what name were the popular, unisex, two-tone Oxford shoes known, as worn by Elvis Presley in *Jailhouse Rock* in 1957?

20. Which iconic 1950s hairstyle for women was first devised by Margaret Vinci Heldt, owner of a Chicago salon, for a national hair styling contest in the US in 1954?

1954 TO 1956
Sporting Events

1. Which team were the FA First Division champions in 1954?

2. Which country hosted the 1954 FIFA World Cup?

3. What European football association was founded in Basel, Switzerland in 1954?

4. Who broke the four-minute mile barrier for the first time in Oxford, in May 1954?

5. Which US heavyweight champion boxer died in December 1954, days after losing consciousness in a fight against Willie James?

6. Which Australian golfer won the British Open in 1954 and would go on to become the only player in the 20th century to secure three consecutive wins in the tournament, repeating his victory in 1955 and 1956?

7. Which US baseball star married Hollywood screen idol, Marilyn Monroe, in 1954?

8. Which American heavyweight defended his World Championship title in 1955?

9. Which team won the Ryder Cup in 1955?

10. Which annual women's golf tournament was launched in 1955?

11. In 1955, which Argentine Formula One driver secured his third consecutive World Championship title, the first racing driver ever to have done so?

12. Which snooker player secured his fourth of five consecutive World Championship titles in 1955?

13. Who won the Five Nations rugby union championship in 1955?

14. Which US tennis star won the Wimbledon Women's final in 1955?

15. Which Austrian ski champion dominated the 1956 Winter Olympics, winning Gold for the men's downhill, slalom and giant slalom?

16. Which national team won the 1956 Winter Olympics, taking home the most medals and the most gold medals?

17. Which American heavyweight boxer retired in 1956, the only heavyweight to have retired with an undefeated, perfect record over his career?

18. Which British tennis player made it to the Wimbledon Women's Final in 1956, where she lost to Shirley Fry Irvine of the US?

19. Which team were FA First Division champions in 1956?

20. Who won the Baseball World Series in 1956?

FIFTIES FICTION
NAME THE
NOVEL

1. J.R.R. Tolkein's first in an epic fantasy adventure series, published in 1954

2. J.D. Salinger's controversial 1951 tale of an angst-ridden teenager named Holden Caufield

3. E.B. White's enduring farmyard children's novel, published in 1952

4. William Golding's cautionary tale of what happens when boys are left to their own devices, published in 1954

5. C.S. Lewis's magical allegorical fantasy for children, published in 1950

6. Ray Bradbury's much-loved 1953 dystopian vision of a book-banning future

7. Vladimir Nabokov's deeply controversial tale of Professor Humbert Humbert, published in 1955

8. Ernest Hemingway's 1952 tale of an ageing Cuban fisherman

9. John Steinbeck's most ambitious novel, published in 1952, which tracks the interconnected lives of two Californian families

10. Jack Kerouac's era-defining Beat Generation travel journal, published in 1957

11. Truman Capote's novella, portraying his most enduring character, published in 1958

12. Dr Seuss' classic spirit of Christmas rhyming tale for children, published in 1957

13. Daniel Keyes' science-fiction short story, published in 1959, and the precursor to a 1966 novel of the same name

14. Boris Pasternak's complex 1957 tale of revolutionary Russia, which was banned from publication in the USSR

15. Patricia Highsmith's first in what would become a series of five psychological thrillers, known collectively as the Ripliad

16. Isaac Asimov's 1950 short science-fiction story collection that explored the interactions of man and machine

17. Mary Norton's children's fantasy tale of a family of tiny people, published in 1952

18. Graham Greene's 1955 anti-war novel

19. Michael Bond's 1958 children's classic, telling of the terribly British adventures of a stowaway from Peru

20. Richard Matheson's 1954 horror novel that was to inspire a new genre of post-apocalyptic zombie horror

FIFTIES IDOLS

ELLA FITZGERALD

1. Ella Fitzgerald was born in Virginia but grew up in which city?

2. Ella Fitzgerald's debut album was a collection of covers of songs by which composer?

3. In December 1954, why did Ella and the members of her band sue Pan Am Airlines?

4. In 1955, Fitzgerald performed at the high-profile Sunset Boulevard club, the Mocambo, at which very few black musicians had ever performed. Who lobbied for her to get the gig?

5. In which 1955 movie did Ella Fitzgerald perform alongside Peggy Lee and Janet Leigh?

6. At a non-segregated Jazz at the Philharmonic concert in Houston, Texas in 1955, Fitzgerald, Dizzie Gillespie and her manager, Norman Granz, were arrested on what charge?

7. In 1956, Fitzgerald left Decca records and signed with which new record label, created around her by her manager, Norman Granz?

8. In 1956 and 1957, Ella recorded two albums with which jazz trumpeter?

9. In 1956, she released the first of a series of eight *Songbook* albums, in each of which she interpreted a different composer. Which composer featured first?

10. Which Gershwin musical did Ella record with Louis Armstrong and Duke Ellington in 1957?

11. In all eight *Songbook* albums, Fitzgerald collaborated with only one composer during the recording process. Which one?

12. Fitzgerald lived temporarily in which European country from 1961 to 1963?

13. In 1959, why did the NBC network request that Norman Granz find an alternative guitarist to Herb Ellis for Ella's live performance on *The Bell Telephone Hour*?

14. For which song did Ella forget the lyrics during a live recording at a concert in Berlin, and improvise so brilliantly she would later win an Emmy?

15. With which iconic American actor and singer did Fitzgerald reportedly love working, although they never recorded an album together?

16. Ella Fitzgerald said, 'I stole everything I ever heard', adding that she mostly stole from what?

17. Which legendary singer did Fitzgerald admit to having visited backstage and asking for an autograph, adding, 'I still don't know if it was the right thing to do'?

18. What did Fitzgerald say was 'the only thing better than singing'?

19. At whose presidential inauguration did Ella Fitzgerald perform in 1961?

20. In the UK, Fitzgerald became the first artist to climb the charts with a Lennon-McCartney cover. What was the song?

FIFTIES HOLLYWOOD

MUSICALS

NAME THAT SONG

1. 'A lady doesn't wander all over the room, And blow on some other guys dice'

2. 'I love all the many charms about you, Above all I want these arms about you'

3. 'My dad said "Be an actor, my son, But be a comical one"'

4. 'A kiss may be grand, But it won't pay the rental'

5. 'The night is bitter, The stars have lost their glitter'

6. 'He will not always say what you will have him say'

7. 'Suntanned, windblown, Honeymooners at last alone'

8. 'Spider Murphy played the tenor saxophone, Little Joe was blowin' on the slide trombone'

9. 'You've got all the qualities of Peter Pan, I'd look far before I'd find a sweeter pan'

10. 'We ain't met yet but I'm a-willing to bet, You're the gal for me'

11. 'A clown with his pants falling down, Or the dance that's a dream of romance'

12. 'Now I shout it from the highest hills, Even told the golden daffodils'

13. 'Fish got to swim and birds got to fly, I got to love one man 'til I die'

14. 'The girls today in society, Go for classical poetry'

15. 'We met at nine. We met at eight. I was on time. No, you were late.'

16. 'You may see a stranger, Across a crowded room'

17. 'They told me to throw some more coal in the boiler. But that don't do no good'

18. 'There's a bright golden haze on the meadow'

19. 'Oh, my mother was frightened by a shotgun they say, That's why I'm such a wonderful shot'

20. 'There's a man in New Orleans who plays rock and roll'

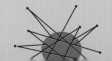

FIFTIES SCI-FI
Movie Classics

1. Which 1950 sci-fi movie is credited with being the first to consider the possible dangers of space travel?

2. Which 1951 movie saw a humanoid alien named Klaatu walk the Earth with an eight-foot tall robot named Gort?

3. In which 1951 movie did an Arctic American Air Base battle against a murderous alien force?

4. In which 1951 movie did a brave band of folk fight to construct a rocket to leave Earth as another planet hurtled towards it on a collision course?

5. Which 1951 sci-fi saw an alien land on the Scottish moors ahead of a full-scale invasion of Earth?

6. Which H.G. Wells story about a Californian town under attack by Martians was adapted for the big screen in 1953?

7. Which 1953 movie adaptation of Ray Bradbury's story, *The Meteor*, follows the adventures of a star-gazing astronaut and his fiancée after an alien craft crashes to Earth?

8. Which 1953 alien sci-fi was the first to be shot in Technicolor?

9. Which 1953 futuristic sci-fi movie looked at space travel set in a

future in which the Earth enjoyed gender equality and the President of the US was a woman?

10. Which Disney adventure, released in 1954 and starring Kirk Douglas, was the first sci-fi film to be released in the widescreen format, CinemaScope?

11. Which 1954 black-and-white sci-fi horror classic about a monster discovered in the Amazonian jungle was shot in 3D?

12. Which 1954 movie was the first of the decade's 'nuclear' monster movies, and depicted an invasion of giant, irradiated ants?

13. Which 1955 British sci-fi from Hammer films was based on a television series of the same name and told of a journey into space that ended in terror?

14. Which 1956 movie starred Leslie Nielsen and Walter Pidgeon in the tale of a starship crew who set out to investigate a far-flung Earth colony after it goes quiet?

15. Which 1956 movie depicted an alien invasion of Earth in a plot inspired by a best-selling non-fiction title, *Flying Saucers From Outer Space*?

16. Which 1956 sci-fi was shot in the style of film noir and depicted an insidious alien invasion in a small Californian town?

17. In which 1957 movie did Grant Williams play a man having an incredibly bad day thanks to the unfortunate effects of radiation and insecticide?

18. Which 1958 movie centres on the most unfortunate bachelor party, in which Tom Tyron plays a young husband-to-be who ends the night abducted by aliens?

19. Which sci-fi horror was released as a double-bill with *I Married a Monster From Outer Space*?

20. In which 1959 movie did Pat Boone and James Mason lead an expedition down through an extinct Icelandic volcano?

FIFTIES

STAGE

PLAYS

1. In which 1956 play does Lavinia leave her husband, Edward, just as they are about to host a party at their London home?

2. In which 1952 play do Old Man and Old Woman prepare chairs for invisible guests?

3. Which thriller opened in London's West End in 1952 and has yet to close?

4. Which 1953 historical play threw a spotlight on Senator McCarthy's claims that there were communist sympathisers at every level of American politics?

5. Who were the 1953 characters Vladimir and Estragon waiting for?

6. Which 1954 Irish play was set in a Dublin prison on the eve of an execution?

7. Which Pulitzer Prize-winning 1954 play featured plantation owner, Big Daddy, his wife, Maggie the Cat, and their son, Brick?

8. Which 1956 play was set in New York, near the Brooklyn Bridge?

9. Which Pulitzer Prize-winning 1956 play examined a long day

in the life of the ill-fated Tyrone family, whose mother, Mary, suffered with a drug addiction?

10. Which 1956 play told of a love triangle, spawning the phrase 'angry young men'?

11. The action of which 1957 play focused on two hitmen called Ben and Gus?

12. Which 1957 play has four unlucky characters who live in dustbins, one of whom can't sit, one of whom can't stand and a couple with no legs?

13. Which play turned a spotlight onto an angry middle-aged man in 1957, at the request of Sir Laurence Olivier?

14. Which 1957 play was set in a conventional community in America's Deep South?

15. Which 1957 British play, penned by a British novelist, was a thriller set among the secretive Callifer family?

16. The action for which 1957 play takes place in a single room, rented by a young married couple?

17. Which 1958 play was set in a run-down boarding house in an English seaside town, with its eclectic mix of occupants?

18. Which 1958 one-act play was originally written as a monologue for Northern Irish actor, Patrick Magee, who plays a 69-year-old man reviewing tapes he recorded thirty years earlier?

19. In which 1958 American play does a New Orleans' family's poor relation, Catharine Holly, appear to have lost her mind following the death of her cousin during a European holiday?

20. Which British thriller opened on a foggy night with a character climbing into a house through an open window, where he finds a woman standing over the body of her husband with a gun in her hand?

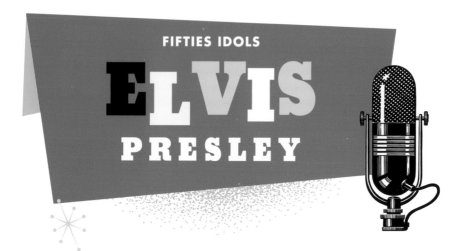

FIFTIES IDOLS

ELVIS
PRESLEY

1. In August 1953, 18-year-old Elvis Presley walked into the offices of which Memphis recording company to hire a studio for just long enough to record two tracks for his mother?

2. What was the first track of Elvis' to have been played on Memphis radio in July 1954?

3. In October 1954, which popular country music radio programme hired Elvis to perform every Saturday night for a year?

4. Which 19-year-old, dark-glasses clad rising star said of seeing Elvis Presley on stage, 'I just didn't know what to make of it. There was just no reference point in the culture to compare it'?

5. Elvis' early musical style was a combination of country music and rhythm and blues. By what name did the style come to be known?

6. Name Elvis' debut album, released with RCA in 1956?

7. Elvis' debut album included his unique take on several rhythm and blues classics, setting the scene for the new rock 'n' roll sound by giving which instrument the lead?

8. As Elvis made a number of television appearances throughout the early months of 1956, what prompted Ed Sullivan to declare him 'unfit for family viewing'?

9. Why was an appearance on NBC's *The Steve Allen Show* in July 1956 considered by Elvis as 'the most ridiculous appearance I ever did'?

10. Which double-A side single stayed at the top of the Billboard charts for a record eleven weeks in 1956?

11. When Presley finally made an appearance on the *Ed Sullivan Show* in September 1956, his performance of which forthcoming new single prompted unprecedented advance sales of a million copies?

12. What was Elvis' first movie, released in November 1956?

13. In 1957, Presley bought an 18-roomed mansion near Memphis, to be closer to his parents. What was it called?

14. Upon the advice of the make-up artist on Presley's second movie, *Loving You* in 1957, what change did Elvis make to his appearance?

15. What did Elvis say 'sure got me into a rut'?

16. Who described rock 'n' roll as 'played and written, for the most part, by cretinous goons', prompting Elvis to respond, 'He is a great success and a fine actor, but I think he shouldn't have said it'?

17. Finish the Elvis quote: 'The Lord can give, and the Lord can take away. I might be. . .next year'

18. What did Elvis say could 'do anything it wants with me', in March 1958?

19. Who did Elvis meet while serving in Germany that was to change his life?

20. Finish the Elvis quote: 'The Army teaches boys to. . .'

FOOD
IN THE
FIFTIES

1. In 1950, with wartime motoring restrictions lifted, a soft drinks company from South Wales reintroduced a now iconic means of sales and distribution. What was it?

2. In the days before the widespread presence of the fridge in British kitchens, what American canned meat became omnipresent?

3. Salmon sandwiches were common at teatime for many families. But in what form was the salmon to be found in the pantry?

4. If the British cuisine saw any dressing on round lettuce, cucumber and tomato salad in the 1950s, what would it have been?

5. What snack was available in waxed paper bags or sealed tins, with the inclusion of a small blue bag of salt for additional flavour?

6. What fast food was commonly sold from wagons outside pubs?

7. What breakfast staples were billed as delicious when 'eaten with anything in the larder that is good to spread'?

8. Which phenomenon in the restaurant industry first came to the UK from America in 1954?

9. What frozen family favourite was first made available in the UK from 1955, popular despite the scarcity of household freezers?

10. By 1958, the increased and widespread popularity of which exotic form of national cookery prompted holiday camp entrepreneur, Billy Butlin, to add a flavoured noodle dish to his camp menus?

11. Which popular teatime treat included a savoury spread, made from fat and meat juices saved from the Sunday roast?

12. Which economical offal-based dish made a regular appearance on most family menus?

13. Which ubiquitous modern kitchen condiment was available in 1950s Britain only from pharmacies, where it was sold as a means of unblocking ear-wax?

14. What staple of modern western cooking is now available in a plethora of varieties, but was available only as a pudding ingredient in 1950s Britain?

15. How would most British households have taken delivery of their daily quota of milk in the era?

16. Grocery shopping in Britain in the 1950s was largely carried out in the same way it had been for generations. What was yet to become a standard feature of shopping for food?

17. At the butcher's shop, or the butchery counter of the Co-op, how would a customer be served their bacon?

18. How was sugar purchased?

19. How did shoppers most commonly pay for their groceries?

20. What were sold for sixpence a quarter at the island counters of Woolworths, aside from sweets?

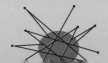

DO YOU REMEMBER THE 1950s?

NAME THE LADY
Fifties Top 20 Hits

1. Whose 'Secret Love' took her to the top spot in the UK in April 1954?

2. Who asked, '(How Much Is) That Doggie In The Window?' in April 1953, becoming the first British woman to reach No. 1?

3. Which American woman sang her way to the top of the UK charts with, 'Little Things Mean A Lot' in September 1954?

4. In November 1954, 'My Son, My Son' was which Forces' Sweetheart's only No. 1 hit?

5. Whose 1958 cover of 'Who's Sorry Now' took her to No. 1 in the UK?

6. Who spent six weeks at the top spot in 1958 with 'Stupid Cupid'?

7. 'This Ole House' put which American actress and cabaret

star at the top of the charts on both sides of the pond in 1954?

8. Who made a hit with a cover of Tin Pan Alley songwriter, Al Sherman's last song, 'Comes A-Long A-Love' in January 1953?

9. Which ragtime pianist scored a hit in December 1954 with 'Let's Have Another Party'?

10. Which Belfast lady crooned, 'Softly, Softly' all the way to No. 1 in February 1955?

11. 'Dreamboat' was a hit for which 'girl with a giggle in her throat' in July 1955?

12. The 'Rock and Roll Waltz' was a hit for which American jazz singer in March 1956?

13. Which Forces' Sweetheart's 'Lay Down Your Arms' was briefly banned by the BBC in September 1956 because they feared it may disincline British forces to fight during the conflict in Cyprus?

14. Who sang 'The Day That The Rains Came' in January 1959?

15. Who made 'As I Love You' the UK's first No. 1 by a Welsh artist in February 1959?

16. Which American Broadway and Opera star had a hit in the UK in 1953 with 'Hold Me, Thrill Me, Kiss Me'?

17. Who had a hit in the UK with 'Under The Bridges of Paris', which she sang in both French and English?

18. Which Scottish folk singer had a hit with 'Freight Train' in 1957?

19. Which American jazz singer and actress added her own, uncredited section of lyrics to her 1958 cover of 'Fever'?

20. Whose 1955 debut single, 'Cry Me a River', peaked just outside the UK Top 20?

BRITISH
CARS
OF THE FIFTIES

1. Which Rover, available from 1949, was known as the 'Cyclops Rover' because of its single fog lamp?

2. Which car is the oldest in the fleet owned by the British Royal Family, and was used to drive Princess Elizabeth and The Duke of Edinburgh from 1950?

3. Which French painter, known for his vivid use of colour, drove a 1951 Chevrolet DeLuxe?

4. Which European Prince, known all over the world for his marriage to a Hollywood screen siren in 1956, drove a 1950 Lincoln Cosmopolitan?

5. Which post-war car was designed to attract a foreign market with American styling, and with an engine that would come to be used in Triumph TR sports cars?

6. Which British wartime Prime Minister was driven around 1950s London in a 1953 Hooper-bodied Bentley R-Type?

7. Which baby Ford hit British car salesrooms in 1953 with a new look for a new era and a range of upbeat, Festival-of-Britain colours?

8. Which 1955 luxury two-seater coupé sported unmistakeable gull-wing doors, the fastest top-speed in the world, and was the car of choice for screen idol, Clark Gable?

9. Which 1955 car was known as 'The Giant Killer', after James Dean died at the wheel in September 1955?

10. Which iconic figure of the era gave his mother a 1955 Cadillac Fleetwood Series 60, which he had painted pink?

11. Which British actress, the UK's answer to Marilyn Monroe, also drove a 1955 Cadillac?

12. Which Welsh actor, known for his stormy relationship with Elizabeth Taylor, favoured a 1955 Cadillac Coupe de Ville?

13. Which screen siren drove a 1956 Thunderbird painted sunset coral around Los Angeles?

14. Which 1957 sports car was the best-selling British sports car in the US?

15. Vauxhall produced an all-American look for a new range of cars from 1957, with bench seating front and back and steering column gear, plenty of chrome and the option to go two-tone. What were they?

16. Which Spanish artist, founder of the Cubist movement, drove a 1957 Lincoln Premier?

17. Which sultry French Hollywood star, who would later become an animal rights activist, drove a humble 1957 Citroen 2CV?

18. Which 1959 small car was designed so that 80 per cent of the floor space could be given over to its passengers and was both an iconic design and a family favourite?

19. In 1959, which much-loved British car became the first to sell a million units?

20. Which Italian actress, much loved by Hollywood, drove a Ford Thunderbird convertible?

INVENTIVE

FIRSTS OF THE FIFTIES

1. In 1950, Frank McNamara launched the Diners Club in the US, and the world's first what?

2. In 1950, an American firm launched the first prototype of which classic stringed instrument?

3. In 1951, the US experimented with a new development in television. In its earliest form it would last only two years, but in time would go global. What was it?

4. In 1951, a scientist at Eastman Kodak discovered the super-adhesive qualities of a substance initially developed by mistake. It was marketed originally as 'Eastman #910'. By what name is it more commonly known?

5. In November 1952, the US took the Cold War arms race a step further, with the world's first test-detonation of which weapon?

6. In 1953, an American frozen food company produced the first pre-packaged, complete frozen what?

7. In 1954, two US companies began the world's first production of what portable item?

8. In 1952, RCA produced which electronic musical instrument?

9. In 1953, the Frigidaire company in the US released for sale the

world's first multicoloured range of what household appliance?

10. In 1954, how did two engineers from Corpus Christi in Texas solve the problem of traditional swing doors being caught in the city's high winds?

11. In 1954, Bell Laboratories in the US announced they had successfully developed a new brand of cell battery that the *New York Times* predicted would one day provide 'limitless energy'. What was it?

12. In 1955, Swiss electrical engineer, George de Mestral, patented his innovative fastener, inspired by the burs that clung to his dog after a woodland walk. What was it?

13. In 1955, a Danish plastic construction toy manufacturer produced its first ever kit, called the 'Town Plan'. What was the toy called?

14. In 1956, an oil- and water-repelling chemical solution was launched onto the domestic market. Under what name was it marketed?

15. In 1956, an American electronics company named Ampex pioneered a new means of recording programmes for television. What was it?

16. In 1957, a Canadian engineer working for Union Carbide Eveready in Cleveland, Ohio, filed a patent for a compact alkaline energy source. What was it?

17. In 1957, a Californian toy manufacturer named Wham-O marketed a plastic version of which Australian bamboo exercise aid that would soon become a global craze?

18. In 1959, Nils Bohlin, patented his design for what new car safety feature, credited with saving an estimated one million lives?

19. In 1959, the Mattel toy company launched a new doll, which would become an iconic and enduring toy. What was it?

20. In 1959, Texas Instruments unveiled a device at an electronics trade fair, which made possible a digital revolution. What was it?

FIFTIES SCREEN IDOLS

JAMES DEAN

1. James Dean's first television appearance was in a commercial in 1950. What was he helping to advertise?

2. Dean dropped out of UCLA to pursue a career in acting, and moved to New York where he worked on the set of the game show, *Beat the Clock.* What was his role on the show?

3. While in New York, Dean studied method acting. Who was his teacher?

4. Which American novelist did Dean meet ahead of being cast in his first lead role in 1954?

5. In 1954, Dean began to develop an interest in which sport?

6. With which Italian actress did Dean become romantically involved while he was shooting *East of Eden,* and she was on the adjoining set, filming *The Silver Chalice?*

7. Which Hollywood screen idol claimed Dean closely imitated his

lifestyle, acting like him, riding the same motorcycles, playing the bongos and even dating the same woman (Ursula Andress)?

8. What did Dean once describe as 'fast and clean and you get to go out in a blaze of glory'?

9. What did Dean say he believed to be the 'only greatness for man'?

10. Which American screenwriter was Dean's closest friend and later, his biographer?

11. During the filming of the 1956 Warner Brothers movie, *Giant*, what was Dean contractually banned from doing?

12. In which 1955 movie did Dean declare, 'You're tearing me apart!'?

13. In which 1955 movie did Dean confess, 'I've been jealous all my life'?

14. In which 1956 movie did Dean take method acting so far that he reportedly hardly changed out of his costume for the whole shoot, even making a road safety commercial in his costume?

15. In which movie did Dean yell, 'I'm a rich 'un!' before punching Rock Hudson in the stomach?

16. With which star did Dean reportedly have difficult off-screen relations during the shooting of *Giant*?

17. What did a coroner rule had been the cause of James Dean's fatal car accident on 30th September, 1955?

18. What became of the Porsche Spider in which Dean was killed?

19. Which accolade was Dean the first to receive posthumously?

20. Which 1980's soap opera character was said to have been directly inspired by Dean's portrayal of Jett Rink in *Giant*?

MEDICAL
FIRSTS IN THE FIFTIES

1. In 1950, 49-year-old Ruth Tucker, an American woman with kidney disease, became the first person to undergo which landmark procedure?

2. In 1950, a French pharmacist synthesized a number of compounds to create a pharmaceutical treatment for the common cold. What were they?

3. In 1952, a vaccine developed by American virologist, Jonas Salk, was rolled out for the first time. What was it?

4. In 1952, a new antibiotic was first introduced which would treat respiratory tract and other infections in patients allergic to penicillin. What was it?

5. In 1953, a groundbreaking piece of surgical apparatus was used on a human for the first time, designed by John Gibbon and his wife. It enabled previously unthinkable surgery to be undertaken. What was the apparatus?

6. What surgical procedure did the same piece of apparatus enable?

7. What medical advance was made by James Watson and Francis Crick in 1953?

8. In 1954, which procedure was successfully undertaken between living patients for the first time?

9. In 1954, scientific research provided the first firm evidence of the carcinogenic properties of what?

10. In 1954, American scientist John Rock and endocrinologist, Gregory Pincus conducted successful human trials on 50 women from Massachusetts, of which new pharmaceutical?

11. In 1955, which new antibiotic was made available for the first time, in the treatment of conditions such as acne, chlamydia and syphilis?

12. Which scientific technique, initially devised solely for its military applications, was used as a diagnostic tool in medicine for the first time in 1956?

13. Which national organisation was founded in 1956 as a result of an advertisement placed in *The Times* 'for the promotion of the Dick-Read system'?

14. What did scientists successfully isolate from the human pituitary gland in 1956?

15. In 1957, what development did John Sheehan's work with penicillin result in?

16. In 1957, what crucial aspect of the human immune system was discovered by Alick Isaacs and Jean Lindenmann?

17. In 1958, two scientists from Bell Laboratories in New Jersey filed a patent for a concept they labelled an 'optical maser'. By what name is their invention better known?

18. In 1958, the Cleveland Clinic carried out which coronary procedure for the first time?

19. In 1959, the international medical community was informed about the first successful implantation of which artificial medical aid?

20. In 1959, a French geneticist named Jérôme Lejeune first used chromosome analysis to identify which genetic disorder?

MORE
INVENTIVE
FIRSTS OF THE
FIFTIES

1. In 1950, a Wisconsin company launched the 'Electronic Secretary', the first successful example of what?

2. In 1951, the Chrysler Corporation launched the first range of cars to include which technological innovation?

3. In 1951, cameras became available with which new feature?

4. In 1952, a patent was issued for which 'Classifying Apparatus and Method', to simplify the checkout process for the food retail industry?

5. In 1952, a new personal hygiene product used technology designed for the ballpoint pen. What was it?

6. In 1952, a ginger ale company in New York launched what product aimed at the diabetic market?

7. What was remarkable about a movie released in December, 1952 entitled *Bwana Devil,* about two man-eating lions?

8. What was significant about a new tea, released in 1953, named 'Rose Redi-Tea'?

9. Prompted by several high-profile airline crashes, what was invented by an Australian engineer named David Warren in 1953?

10. In 1954, which scientifically adapted kitchen essential was released onto the market for the first time?

11. Why was the launch of USS *Nautilus* a landmark in military history in 1954?

12. Which range of kitchen appliance was launched in 1954 under the brand name, 'Radar Range', a reference to its use of a form of power first designed for radar during the Second World War?

13. Why did the 'Zenith Flash-matic' revolutionise home entertainment from 1956?

14. In 1959, a Canadian company launched a new form of transportation, designed for very specific climates. What was it?

15. What launch in 1959 was described by the BBC as marking a 'new era in transport'?

16. What new product was launched by the Mistake Out Company in 1956, that would make life significantly simpler for students and secretaries?

17. In 1956, IBM launched a new mechanical means of keeping business accounts instantly available, paper-free. It weighed more than a ton and was larger than a standard refrigerator, but would revolutionise the computer industry. What was it?

18. In 1957, two irrepressible engineers from New Jersey finally found a market use for two plastic shower curtains sealed together, initially intending to create high-tech wallpaper. What was it?

19. What technological advancement was launched commercially in 1958, initially as a means of connecting the SAGE defence system of radar, air bases and control centres, across North America?

20. A record label in the US released four vinyl records in 1958 that were notable for which feature?

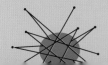

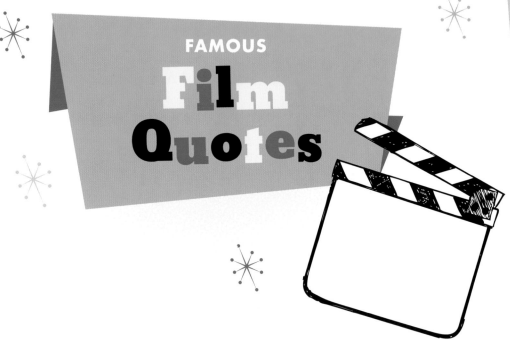

FAMOUS
Film
Quotes

Who said it and in what film?

1. 'You won't bore him, honey. You won't even get a chance to talk.'

2. 'I *am* big. It's the *pictures* that got small.'

3. 'That's, uh, quite a dress you almost have on...What holds it up?'

4. 'I love you. I've loved you since the first moment I saw you. I guess maybe I've even loved you before I saw you.'

5. 'An intellectual carrot! The mind boggles.'

6. 'You risk your skin catchin' killers and the juries turn 'em loose so

72

they can come back and shoot at ya again. If you're honest, you're poor your whole life, and in the end you wind up dyin' all alone on some dirty street. For what? For nothin'. For a tin star.'

7. 'I never knew it could be like this. Nobody ever kissed me the way you do.'

8. 'I just love finding new places to wear diamonds.'

9. 'The Mouth of Truth. Legend is that if you're given to lying, you put your hand in there, it'll be bitten off.'

10. 'I could've had class. I could've been a contender. I could've been somebody, instead of a bum, which is what I am.'

11. 'Hello, everybody. This is *Mrs. Norman Maine*.'

12. 'You're tearing me apart!'

13. 'When I shall sit, you shall sit. When I shall kneel, you shall kneel. Et cetera, et cetera, et cetera.'

14. 'Why didn't you tell me? If it had to happen to one of us, why did it have to be you?'

15. 'I don't want to stop. I like it. Take the picture, take the picture!'

16. 'Yes, smaller than the smallest, I meant something too. To God, there is no zero. I STILL EXIST!'

17. 'You know what I feel like? I feel all the time like a cat on a hot tin roof.'

18. 'Carlotta's necklace, there was where you made your mistake, Judy. You shouldn't keep souvenirs of a killing.'

19. 'That's funny. . .That plane's dustin' crops where there ain't no crops.'

20. 'Mr Allen, this may come as a shock to you, but there are some men who don't end every sentence with a proposition.'

FIFTIES SCREEN IDOLS

MARILYN
MONROE

1. What was Marilyn's official name until she changed it legally in 1956?

2. Which rising Hollywood star was Marilyn's roommate in Hollywood when they were both starting out?

3. The movie studios provided Monroe with vocal coaching in her early career. For what purpose?

4. Marilyn appeared on the front cover of the inaugural edition of which American magazine in 1953?

5. Upon hearing that she had not been cast as the lead in her latest movie in 1953, Marilyn replied, 'Well whatever I am, I'm still the blonde'. What was the movie?

6. In which 1953 movie did Marilyn Monroe make her big screen debut, earning less than the make-up man?

7. Which baseball star married Marilyn Monroe in 1954 at City Hall, San Francisco?

8. Which 1955 movie includes the iconic scene in which Marilyn stands over a subway grate and lets the breeze lift up her skirts?

9. For which American playwright did Marilyn convert to Judaism prior to their wedding in June 1956?

10. After taking lessons with Lee Strasberg at the Actors Studio in 1955, Monroe impressed critics with a dramatic role in which 1956 movie?

11. Which 1930s blonde bombshell did Marilyn describe as her idol?

12. Which two individuals were the largest beneficiaries of Monroe's will?

13. By the time of her death, Marilyn's home included a 400-strong collection of what?

14. Which movie role did Monroe lose to Audrey Hepburn in 1961?

15. Which black singing legend was permitted to perform at many high profile, segregated music venues thanks to the intervention of her close friend, Marilyn Monroe?

16. What did Marilyn once describe as 'wonderful, but you can't curl up with it on a cold night?'

17. Marilyn once said she hoped to have the courage to grow old without what?

18. To what was Marilyn referring when she said it would be nice to have one 'who looks so young and good-looking'?

19. Which scientist's 'Introductory Lectures' did Marilyn Monroe describe as 'genius' and 'so understandable'?

20. About whom did Marilyn once pledge, 'I'll never embarrass him'?

THIRTY FIFTIES
Number One Hits

Name the Singer Most Associated with the Song

1. 'She Wears Red Feathers'

2. 'I See The Moon'

3. 'Such a Night'

4. 'Cara Mia'

5. 'Three Coins in a Fountain'

6. 'Stranger in Paradise'

7. 'Hernando's Hideaway'

8. 'Sixteen Tons'

9. 'Memories Are Made of This'

10. 'Why Do Fools Fall In Love'

11. 'Just Walking In The Rain'

12. 'Singing The Blues'

13. 'Young Love'

14. 'Diana'

15. 'Puttin' On The Style'

16. 'That'll Be The Day'

17. 'Magic Moments'

18. 'It's Only Make Believe'

19. 'All I Have To Do Is Dream'

20. 'It's All In The Game'

21. 'Smoke Gets In Your Eyes'

22. 'All Shook Up'

23. 'Great Balls of Fire'

24. 'Jailhouse Rock'

25. 'It Doesn't Matter Any More'

26. 'Dream Lover'

27. 'Only Sixteen'

28. 'Livin' Doll'

29. 'What Do You Want To Make Those Eyes At Me For'

30. 'What Do You Want?'

OPPORTUNITY
KNOCKS

1. Where did the show make its debut in 1949?

2. Which British comic genius and Goon made his radio debut on *Opportunity Knocks* in 1949?

3. According to Hughie Green's autobiography, which female singing star of the 1950s, known for the 'giggle in her voice', was turned down for the radio show before her career launched?

4. Green also claimed that a much-loved British comedian of the 1950s, known for his regular half hour of radio comedy genius, failed to get through the audition process for the radio version of *Opportunity Knocks*. Who was he?

5. Which radio station picked up the show in the early 1950s?

6. Who was the show's creator and presenter from 1949 until 1978?

7. What was his nationality?

8. The show's presenter first became a household name in the UK after

he became the host of which television quiz show in 1955?

9. The panel of judges would travel around the country to attend the regional auditions by which mode of transport?

10. Which English singer, whose career was catapulted to success with the 1967 record, 'Release Me', failed to get through the auditions for *Opportunity Knocks* in the 1950s?

11. Which English 'easy listening' star, often referred to as 'Mr Moonlight' after his first hit record, 'Give Me the Moonlight', was discovered in the early 1950s on the radio version of *Opportunity Knocks?*

12. Which piece of apparatus was introduced to the show in 1956, as a means of measuring the audience reaction to each act?

13. What catchphrase was associated with this piece of apparatus?

14. When the show transferred to television in 1956, how was voting carried out each week to decide the winner?

15. In which English city were episodes of the ITV show filmed from 1956?

16. Which Northern Irish comedian won *Opportunity Knocks* three times in the 1960s, going on to become a household name on British television?

17. Which British comic legend secured his big break with an *Opportunity Knocks* appearance in 1967?

18. For which catchphrase was presenter Hughie Green most commonly known?

19. Green was disciplined by ITV in the 1970s for using the programme as a platform for what?

20. In the 1970s, which mod-revival English band failed the auditions for *Opportunity Knocks?*

GREAT QUOTES FROM THE FIFTIES

Who said it?

1. 'The reason why we find ourselves in a position of impotency is not because the enemy has sent men to invade our shores, but rather because of the traitorous actions of those who have had all the benefits that the wealthiest nation on earth has had to offer...'

2. 'We are prepared to consider and, if convinced, to accept the abrogation of national sovereignty, provided that we are satisfied with the conditions and the safeguards ... national sovereignty is not inviolable, and it may be resolutely diminished for the sake of all men in all the lands finding their way home together.'

3. 'There is no test for progress other than its impact on the individual.'

4. '...that the United Kingdom should join a federation on the continent of Europe. This is something which we know, in our bones, we cannot do...For Britain's story and her interests lie far beyond the continent of Europe.'

5. 'I like Ike'

6. 'He suddenly opened his eyes and looked at everyone in the room. It was a terrible gaze, mad or maybe furious and full of fear of death...'

7. 'Against the dark background of

the atomic bomb, the United States does not wish merely to present strength, but also the desire and the hope for peace.'

8. 'Senator; you've done enough. Have you no sense of decency, sir, at long last? Have you no sense of decency?'

9. 'Don't bother just to be better than your contemporaries or predecessors. Be better than yourself.'

10. 'Our quarrel is not with Egypt, still less with the Arab world. It is with Colonel Nasser.'

11. 'Gertrude Stein did us the most harm when she said, "You're all a lost generation." That got around to certain people and we all said, "Whee! We're lost."'

12. 'Indeed let us be frank about it – most of our people have never had it so good.'

13. 'It is therefore not a question of who is in favour of the hydrogen bomb, but a question of what is the most effective way of getting the damn thing destroyed.

14. 'Life's most persistent and urgent question is: "What are you doing for others?"'

15. 'The pattern of the Commonwealth is changing and with it is changing Britain's position as the Mother Country. Our children are growing up.'

16. 'Always do sober what you said you'd do drunk. That will teach you to keep your mouth shut.'

17. 'Henry James is the maestro of the semicolon. Hemingway is a first-rate paragrapher. From the point of view of ear, Virginia Woolf never wrote a bad sentence.'

18. 'Poor Eisenhower, I am just beginning to understand what his problems are.'

19. 'We have existed not quite 42 years and in another 7 years, we will be on the same level as America. When we catch you up, in passing you by, we will wave to you.'

20. 'All you can be sure about in a political-minded writer is that if his work should last you will have to skip the politics when you read it.'

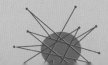

FOOTBALL IN THE FIFTIES

1. Which nation hosted the FIFA World Cup in 1950?

2. Why did India withdraw from the 1950 World Cup at short notice?

3. Why was one of the 1950s World Cup group matches known afterwards as 'The Miracle on the Grass'?

4. Which nation won the FIFA World Cup in Switzerland in 1954?

5. Which favourites to win the 1954 World Cup were defeated, much to everyone's surprise?

6. Which host nation were defeated by Brazil in the final of the 1958 FIFA World Cup?

7. Which legendary player made his first appearance at the 1958

World Cup, at the age of just 17-years-old?

8. What was particularly noteworthy about the UK presence at the 1958 World Cup?

9. Why was the 1958 World Cup remembered as Wales' finest moment in football history?

10. Which star Welsh player was out injured, setting them at a disadvantage in the quarter finals?

11. Why did Pelé break Welsh hearts in 1958?

12. Who took over as manager of Second Division Liverpool FC in 1959, transforming them into a major force in the sport?

13. Which player was a dominant force throughout the decade, known as 'The Wizard of the Dribble' and, 'The Magician'? He would also go on to become the only player to be knighted while still playing top-level football.

14. The 1953 FA Cup Final between Blackpool and Bolton Wanderers was widely known afterwards as 'The Matthews Final', because of the performance of Blackpool's Stanley Matthews. But which other Blackpool player made history by scoring a hat trick in the second half for the only time in FA Cup Final history?

15. Which manager stamped his mark on Manchester United throughout the decade?

16. Which team were described as 'The World's Best Team' in 1954?

17. Which football tournament took place in 1956 for the first time?

18. Which club won the tournament?

19. Which 19-year-old player made his debut with Manchester United in 1957?

20. What tragedy struck the Manchester United team in 1958?

FIFTIES SCREEN IDOLS

Marlon Brando

1. What is Brando widely credited for having brought to the craft of acting in the 1950s?

2. Brando once quit a job as an elevator boy in a department store because he was too embarrassed to call out the name of which floor?

3. A 1951 screen adaptation of which Tennessee Williams' play first brought Brando to international attention?

4. Which British actress would Brando confess to having been attracted to during the filming of the same movie, adding that he kept his feelings to himself out of respect for Laurence Olivier?

5. In the 1952 movie, *Viva Zapata!*, Brando said he felt hostility from his co-star, Anthony Quinn. Only years later did the two men compare notes and discover the reason. What was it?

6. Which Shakespearean character did Brando play in a 1953 movie?

7. Which 1953 movie saw Brando become a cultural icon, popularising the leather biker look for a generation and inspiring emerging actors such as James Dean?

8. In the same movie, Brando rode his own motorbike. What was it?

9. Brando later reflected that his character in the same movie was the one to whom he felt he could most relate. He said he empathised especially with the line, 'Nobody tells me. . .', what?

10. Brando initially turned down the offer of his iconic role in the 1954 movie, *On the Waterfront*, which was very nearly played by Frank Sinatra. What were his reasons?

11. Who was his female co-star in *On The Waterfront*?

12. Of which (improvised) scene from the same movie did director Elia Kazan say, 'If there is a better performance by a man in the history of film in America, I don't know what it is'?

13. Brando won an Academy Award for Best Actor for his performance in *On the Waterfront*. What did he use the award for?

14. Which Hollywood actress presented Brando with his Oscar in 1955?

15. Which 1955 movie was Brando's first – and only – musical?

16. Which co-star from the same movie described Brando as 'the world's most over-rated actor' and nicknamed him, 'Mumbles'?

17. Finish the Brando quotation: 'Would people applaud me if I were a good. . .'

18. Which 1957 movie attracted controversy for its open discussion of interracial marriage, although it earned Brando an Academy Award nomination for Best Actor?

19. Brando once admitted to being a sensitive sort, saying 'If there are two hundred people in a room and one of them doesn't like me, I've got to. . .', what?

20. In which 1958 movie did Brando dye his hair blonde and adopt a German accent, clashing with the writer because of his interpretation of the character, who he refused to portray as 'inherently bad'?

SCHOOL DAYS

1. In the 1950s classroom, when children were deemed old enough to progress to writing in ink, what was most commonly used?

2. Which 'look-and-say' reading scheme was first introduced in the UK in 1949, and dominated the British classroom throughout the decade?

3. Which popular brand of children's books came with an open-winged insect logo and a dust-wrapper throughout the 1950s (dropping the dust-wrapper and adopting a closed-wing version of the logo in the 1960s)?

4. Many British primary schools in the decade would dedicate a period of the day to what activity, now long since abandoned?

5. British schools throughout the decade would receive regular visits from medical staff, who would carry out a particular health inspection of every pupil. What were these visitors commonly known as?

6. What supplement was routinely dished out to schoolchildren, and almost universally loathed?

7. Most girls were subjected to which uncomfortable undergarment, especially throughout the winter months?

8. What caused a red ring to form around children's legs by the end of a school day?

9. What was dished out to every pupil in $^1/_3$ pint bottles daily, whether the child wanted it or not?

10. In the early years of the decade, while food rationing was still in place, what featured most commonly on school dinner plates?

11. The majority of primary schools around the country had two entrances. What was often written above each entrance?

12. How did many teachers in the period dress for school?

13. The final year of junior school education was dominated by preparation for what rite of passage?

14. What was the most feared outcome of this rite of passage?

15. What was most notable about school bathroom facilities in the 1950s?

16. School uniform for boys enforced what garment, all year round, until the age of 11?

17. What post-war social phenomenon caused class sizes in the 1950s to swell, often to as many as 50 pupils?

18. With such large classes, and a single adult in every classroom, what was a common feature of maintaining order?

19. The teaching of arithmetic routinely involved which method of learning?

20. What happened in every school every time the Head Master or Head Mistress entered a classroom?

SOUNDS
OF THE FIFTIES

1. Which song was originally recorded by both Gene Autry and The Glenn Miller Orchestra before Fats Domino found his thrill?

2. Which American R&B vocalist was known as 'Mr Personality' and topped the charts in 1959 with 'Stagger Lee'?

3. In the 1957 Everly Brothers hit, 'Wake Up Little Susie', what was the curfew time for the young couple who fell asleep at the movies?

4. True or false: Little Richard was nearly six feet tall?

5. Which Bobby Darin smash hit was only written for a bet?

6. Which American girl group is best remembered for the hits 'Will You Love Me Tomorrow' and 'Tonight's the Night'?

7. Which American disc jockey was known as 'Moondog'?

8. Willa Mae Thornton recorded the original version of which seminal 1956 Elvis Presley hit, subsequently hailed 'an emblem of the rock 'n' roll revolution'?

9. Which rock 'n' roll legend was born on 7th September, 1936, in Lubbock, Texas?

10. In 1952, who launched his career with 'Three O' Clock Blues'?

11. Which American rock 'n' roll star died in St Martin's Hospital in Bath, UK on Easter Sunday, 17th April, 1960.

12. Which American singer songwriter was known as the 'Queen of Rockabilly'?

13. In which US state was Elvis Presley born?

14. What was Cliff Richard's first No. 1 single?

15. In 1958, the six-piece American doo-wop close harmony group The Monotones became a one hit wonder with which song?

16. How was Jiles P. Richardson better known?

17. In 1952, Jo Stafford became the first female artist to reach No. 1 in the UK Singles Chart, with which song?

18. How is American R&B and Chicago Blues vocalist and guitarist Ellas Otha Bates better known?

19. Which rock 'n' roll classic was first issued in May 1954 as the B-side to 'Thirteen Women (and Only One Man in Town)' and was initially considered a commercial flop?

20. What was Chuck Berry's first hit single?

CRICKET
IN THE FIFTIES

1. Which team asserted their dominance at the 1950 Test Series, winning 3–1?

2. Which Trinidad-born calypso singer burst into a spontaneous celebratory song entitled, 'Victory Test Match' upon seeing his national team win at Lord's in 1950, leading a dancing parade of jubilant cricket fans through the streets as far as Piccadilly?

3. Who became the first professional cricketer to captain the England team in 1952?

4. Under his captaincy, what did England achieve in 1953, for the first time in 19 years?

5. Which player took a key part in the Ashes win of 1953, and was also a double international, playing football with the England team?

6. Who won the Ashes 3–1 in 1954?

7. What was the significance of the 1954 Ashes victory?

8. Which cricketer played for England throughout the decade, and has since been hailed as one of the greatest bowlers in cricketing history?

9. Which player was named 'Cricketer of the Year' in 1954, as well as being accused of being a chucker against Barbados in the same year?

10. Which 17-year-old player made his Test Debut for the West Indies against England in March 1954?

11. Who made his first and only Test appearance for Pakistan against England in 1954, the youngest player ever to have played just a single Test match, at 16 years and 352 days old?

12. Which England cricketer of the era was named 'Typhoon' by the British press, regarded by many as one of the fastest bowlers in the sport?

13. In 1956, what did Jim Laker achieve in a Test match at Old Trafford against Australia?

14. Cricket in the 1950s has been described as a slow, safety-conscious affair. The decade saw eight of the top ten matches with the all-time lowest what?

15. Which team dominated County Cricket throughout the 1950s?

16. Who were the same team's three star players through the 1950s?

17. Who captained the team from 1952 to 1958, winning the county championship title every year?

18. Which English team finally stopped playing the sport in 1957, after 60 years?

19. Which international cricketing body was first established in 1958?

20. Which team won the Ashes in 1958-9?

FAMOUS Film Quotes

Who said it and in what film?

1. 'Funny business, a woman's career – the things you drop on your way up the ladder so you can move faster. You forget you'll need them again when you get back to being a woman.'

2. 'Well, I wrestled with reality for 35 years, Doctor. And I'm happy to state I finally won out over it.'

3. 'Your choice is simple: join us and live in peace, or pursue your present course and face obliteration. We shall be waiting for your answer.'

4. 'Whoever you are, I have always depended on the kindness of strangers.'

5. 'Clowns are funny people, they only love once.'

6. 'Ladies and Gentlemen. Stop that girl. That girl running up the

aisle - stop her. That's the girl whose voice you heard and loved tonight. She's the real star of the picture. Kathy Selden.'

7. 'Excuse me, but what is the way to Europe, France?'

8. 'The way most people go about it, they use more brains picking a horse in the third at Belmont than they do picking a husband.'

9. '"Hey, Johnny, what are you rebelling against" "Whaddya got?"'

10. 'You know, in the old days, they used to put your eyes out with a red-hot poker. Any of those bikini bombshells you're always watchin' with a red-hot poker?'

11. 'The pellet with the poison's in the flagon with the dragon; the vessel with the pestle has the brew that is true.'

12. 'See, dogs like us, we ain't such dogs as we think we are.'

13. 'Come on, partner. Why don't you kick off your spurs?'

14. 'The slaves are mine. Their lives are mine, all that they own is mine. I do not know your God, nor will I let Israel go.'

15. 'Do not speak to me of rules. This is war! This is not a game of cricket!'

16. 'Well, that's silly, honey. People just don't get smaller.'

17. 'There's no hope for him now, Travis. He's suffering. You know we've got to do it.'

18. 'Mr Quick, I am a human being. Do you know what that means?'

19. 'Your eyes are full of hate, Forty-One. That's good. Hate keeps a man alive.'

20. 'Now you've done it! Now you have done it!. . .You tore off one of my chests.'

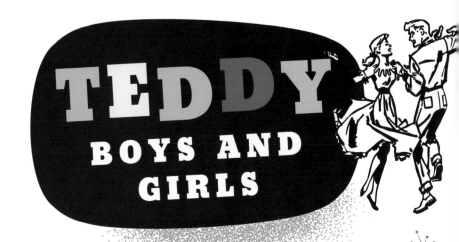

TEDDY
BOYS AND
GIRLS

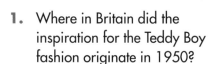

1. Where in Britain did the inspiration for the Teddy Boy fashion originate in 1950?

2. Who were the Cosh Boys?

3. Who played the female lead in the 1952 British movie, *Cosh Boy*?

4. What were Finger-tip Drapes?

5. What incident, on London's Clapham Common in July 1952, prompted the British press to make a connection between, 'Flick knives, dance music and Edwardian suits'?

6. By which girl's name were Teddy Girls often collectively known?

7. Which 1954 big band number by bandleader Ken Mackintosh lent its name to British Teddy Boys before their association with rock 'n' roll?

8. Which accessory was favoured by Teddy Girls, worn at the neck?

9. By 1954, what proportion of a typical London teenager's wage was it estimated that a full

Edwardian-style suit would have cost a well-dressed Ted?

10. In September 1956, which American band had five records in the British Top 20, sealing the link between the Teddy Boy and rock 'n' roll?

11. What American Western-inspired adaptation to the Edwardian style were British Teddy Boys inspired to make?

12. Over the Easter weekend, 1954, which British coastal resort was the scene of violent clashes between gangs of what the press described as 'Edwardian thugs', many of whom had come from London's East End?

13. What style of hat was favoured by early Teddy Girls?

14. Which freelance photographer (a future film director) published a series of documentary photographs entitled 'Teddy Girl' in the *Picture Post* in 1955?

15. A report into Scotland Yard's investigation into Teddy Boy culture in *Illustrated Magazine* in 1955, speculated that the Edwardian style reflected an attempt by teenage boys to assert their manhood, due to which post-war societal change?

16. Teddy girls completed their look by carrying which practical accessory, regardless of whether or not the weather called for it?

17. Which 1956 movie premiere at the Trocadero Cinema in London's Elephant and Castle saw Teddy Boys and Girls riot and slash seats with flick knives?

18. After which Hollywood movie star was a popular Teddy Boy hairstyle named?

19. What was 'The Boston'?

20. Whose 1958 novel, *Teddy Boy* sensationalised the violence of Teddy Boy gangs?

THE
OLYMPICS

1. Where did the 1952 Summer Olympics take place?

2. Which two states were represented at the 1952 Summer Olympics for the first time in history?

3. A total of 39 out of 40 competitors from one national team arrived too late to compete. What was the team?

4. Which national team failed to win a single gold medal at the 1952 Summer Olympics, for the only time in its history?

5. In which European city did the 1952 Winter Olympics take place?

6. Which two nations competed at the 1952 Winter Olympics for the first time?

7. Where were the 1956 Summer Olympics held?

8. What made this location significant in Olympic history?

9. Why were the equestrian events held in Stockholm, rather than at the same location as everything else?

10. Many nations refused to compete at the Games, including Egypt and Lebanon, Switzerland and the Netherlands. Which two international situations prompted the boycotts?

11. Why did a polo match at the 1956 Games become known as 'The Blood in the Water' match?

12. What featured as part of the closing ceremony for the first time at the 1956 Summer Games?

13. What was significant about German competitors at the 1956 Games?

14. How did Irish athlete, Rob Delany, make Olympic history at the 1956 Summer Games?

15. What happened when Australian athlete, Ron Clarke, lit the Olympic flame?

16. Where were the 1956 Winter Olympics held?

17. What was unique about the venues for the 1956 Winter Olympics?

18. Which state made its Winter Olympic debut in 1956, and dominated the medals boards?

19. What was significant about the figure skating events at the 1956 Winter Games?

20. What was significant about the audience for the 1956 Winter Games?

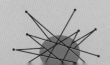

THE Space Race

1. What did representatives of the United States and the Soviet Union announce in press conferences four days apart in the summer of 1955?

2. In the UK, work began in 1955 on the design and construction of a space rocket named *Black Knight*, designed for what military purpose?

3. Both the American and the Soviet early space programmes were built on the science behind which Second World War weapon, originally built by Nazi German scientists?

4. What did Eisenhower fear might be violated by an orbital satellite?

5. What event on 4th October, 1957 marked the start of the Space Race between the Soviet Union and the United States?

6. What was described by an American newsreader on NBC as 'the sound that forever separates the old from the new' in 1957?

7. What US space programme failure was met with headlines such as 'Flopnik' and 'Kaputnik' in December 1957?

8. What scientific discovery was made by *Explorer 1*, the USA's first satellite, launched in January 1958?

9. Which spacecraft, launched in 1959, was the first ever to successfully leave Earth's orbit?

10. What was photographed for the first time by Soviet spacecraft, *Luna 3*, launched in 1959?

11. In May 1959, what key figures in the US Space programme were known as Abel and Miss Baker?

12. Who addressed the world 'from a satellite circling in outer space' on 19th December, 1958, the first time a radio broadcast had ever been transmitted via satellite?

13. What became the world's first successfully launched weather satellite, in February 1959?

14. What were the people of Earth able to witness for the first time in history thanks to the American satellite, *Explorer 6*, in August 1959?

15. What UN Committee was established as a response to the Space Race in December 1959?

16. What was the name given to a new era of design and architecture that reflected the Space Age, popular with American motels and gas stations in the 1950s?

17. Which fictional television character became one of the earliest Space Age heroes in the US and the UK, first appearing on US television in 1950?

18. Which fictional television space hero, adapted from an original comic book storyline, was played by actor Steve Holland from 1954?

19. What was Corona, first launched in June 1959?

20. Which fictional British space hero, described as 'Biggles in Space', made his debut in the comic *Eagle* in 1950 and was serialised on Radio Luxembourg from 1951?

TOP TRACKS BY

FIFTIES BANDS

1. Which US folk group had a hit in 1951 with a cover of 'On Top of Old Smokey'?

2. Which US male vocal group had their first UK hit in 1953 with 'Stranger in Paradise'?

3. Which US rock 'n' roll band had British Teddies rocking in the aisles with 'Rock Around the Clock' in 1954?

4. Which US band had their only hit in 1954 with the track, 'Sh-Boom'?

5. Which US all-female *a capella* band had a hit in the UK and the US with 'Mr Sandman'?

6. Which US vocal group had their first UK No. 1 in November 1955 with 'Great Pretender'?

7. Which US female trio had a UK hit in 1955 with 'Sincerely'?

8. Which US singer and band had a 1957 No. 1 in the UK with 'That'll Be The Day'?

9. 'Little Darlin' was the only UK hit for which Canadian doo-wop male vocal group in 1957?

10. 'All I Have to do is Dream' was a first UK No. 1 in 1958 for which US duo?

11. Which US band released 'In The Still of the Night' in 1956, which became one of the best-known and most enduring doo-wop songs of the era?

12. In 1956, the world's first all-teenaged vocal group had an international success with the record, 'Why Do Fools Fall in Love'. Who were they?

13. Which US doo-wop group had a 1957 hit with 'Come Go With Me'?

14. For which band was the largely instrumental track, 'Tequila', a huge hit on both sides of the Atlantic in 1958?

15. Which San Francisco band had an international hit in 1958 with a cover of 'Tom Dooley', launching a folk revival into the 1960s?

16. Which US group had a 1958 hit with 'For Your Precious Love', but is best known for the 1963 hit, 'It's All Right'?

17. Which US band had a string of British hits throughout the decade, but are perhaps best remembered for their 1959 cover of 'I Only Have Eyes For You'?

18. After a hugely successful decade in the Billboard charts, which US vocal group finally released a UK hit in 1959 with 'Dance With Me', before becoming an international phenomenon throughout the 1960s and 1970s?

19. Which US vocal group had a string of UK hits, such as 'Yakety-Yak' (1958) and 'Charlie Brown' (1959)?

20. Which jazz quartet had a hit in 1959 with what would become a jazz classic and the biggest selling jazz track of all time, 'Take Five'?

1957 to 1959

SPORTING
EVENTS

1. Which legend of British football made his last appearance with the England team in 1957?

2. In 1957, which team won the First Division and only narrowly missed out on winning the FA Cup title too, losing 2–1 to Aston Villa?

3. In 1957, which US baseball player retired from the sport, rather than leave the Brooklyn Dodgers to play for the New York Giants?

4. Which US golfer dominated Women's golf in 1957, winning the Women's Western Open, the Titleholder's Championship and the LPGA Tour?

5. Which nation won the Grand Slam at the 1957 Five Nations tournament?

6. The 1957 Wimbledon Men's final saw two Australian players pitched against each other. The runner-up, Ashley Cooper, won the Australian Open in the same year. Which player secured the Wimbledon title?

7. In 1958, the Manchester United football team were involved in an air disaster at Munich airport. How many players were lost as a result of the crash?

8. Which five-times Argentine Formula

One champion was kidnapped by Cuban rebels in 1958?

9. Which British tennis player reached the Women's Finals at Wimbledon in 1958, where she was defeated by US player, Althea Gibson?

10. In which city were the 1958 British Empire and Commonwealth Games held?

11. Which international sports federation was founded in Marseilles in 1958?

12. Which British couple won the ice dancing championship title at the World Figure Skating Championship in 1958?

13. Which team won the 1958 FIFA World Cup?

14. Which South African cricket team set an as-yet unbroken record for the lowest aggregate score by a first class side, in a Currie Cup match in London against Natal in 1959?

15. Which South African golfer won the British Open in 1959?

16. Which US golfer won the Women's Western Open, the LPGA Championship and the LPGA Tour in 1959?

17. Which British Formula One racing driver, Britain's first Formula One Champion in 1958, was killed in a road traffic accident in January 1959?

18. Which nation had their first outright win at the Five Nations rugby union tournament in 1959?

19. What nationality was Maria Bueno, winner of the Wimbledon Women's Final in 1959?

20. In the third round of the 1959 World Heavyweight Championship fight Swedish boxer, Ingemar Johansson, knocked out an American who three years earlier had been the youngest boxer ever to win the world heavyweight title. Who was he?

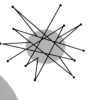

TOYS
AND GAMES

1. Which range of model die-cast and tinplate locomotives and carriages was hugely popular in the first half of the 1950s?

2. Which board game, originally designed to pass the time in air raid shelters, was hugely popular throughout the 1950s?

3. Which character from children's literature inspired a range of appealing Pelham Puppets in the 1950s?

4. In 1950, which much-loved brand of die-cast toy cars and trucks released their 'Guy Vans' range?

5. Which range of die-cast model cars were sold in boxes similar to those containing household matches, the best-selling example of which was a model of the Queen's Coronation Coach in 1953?

6. Which model-making kit first appeared on UK shelves in 1953, with a model of Sir Francis Drake's *The Golden Hind* and a Spitfire Mk1?

7. Which enduring board game was launched in the UK by J.W. Spears and Sons in 1953?

8. Which plastic construction toy was first introduced in the UK in 1955, although it was slow to take off until the following decade?

9. Which modelling clay had its origins in a paste designed to remove coal residue from wallpaper?

10. Which dice game hit stores in its current form in the US in 1956, quickly spreading worldwide?

11. Which Swansea-based toy car manufacturer launched in 1956 took its name from a royal pet?

12. In 1957, which model car-racing kit caused a sensation at the Harrogate Toy Fair because of its innovative system of grooves and electrical current?

13. In which economical and accessible form were dolls available throughout the decade, often incorporated into the advertising of household products, or in magazines and children's comics?

14. Which plastic, circular toy was first manufactured in the US in 1958, but within two years had become a global craze, resulting in the sale of over 100 million units?

15. Which popular pavement toy was often decorated with coloured chalks, and in many regions of the country was seen as a springtime activity only, with 'smugging' (confiscation) coming to those who played out of season?

16. Children of the era enjoyed collecting, swapping and playing with a particular variety of cards, made available in what product?

17. What name was commonly given to large marbles, particularly large silver marbles?

18. Which enduring pavement game, with its origins in Ancient Rome, was sketched out in chalks and could be played by a number of children or solo?

19. Which playground game involved running from one side to another, attempting to avoid those in the centre?

20. Which unlikely toy – an anthropomorphic vegetable – first appeared in the US in 1952, but was initially a kit to which children had to add their own vegetable?

THE Queen's Coronation

1. Where did the coronation take place?

2. Queen Mary died before the coronation, but she was the first queen ever to have been alive to witness what milestone?

3. What were the four symbolic objects handed to the queen during the ceremony?

4. Which Archbishop of Canterbury performed the ceremony?

5. What was declared the moment the Archbishop placed the crown on the queen's head?

6. In a radio broadcast to the nation, the queen pledged, 'Throughout all my life and with all my heart I shall strive to...'?

7. Three million people lined the streets of London to watch the state coach process past, but a further audience of 20 million people also watched the historic event. How?

8. The guests of note who attended the ceremony required more horse-drawn coaches than the royal household possessed. How were the extra coaches sourced?

9. The royal household was also significantly short of coachmen to drive the coaches. How was this problem resolved?

10. Many people who gathered on the streets recalled seeing members of the Grenadier Guards fainting. They began to help the Guards by throwing what in their direction?

11. In the weeks preceding the coronation, much attention was given in the press to a phrase issued by the Coronation Commission, headed up by Prince Philip. To what did the phrase, 'west of the organ screen' refer?

12. The commission finally acquiesced in the televising debate, on what condition?

13. What were constructed on Pontop Pike in County Durham and Glencairn in the Belfast hills in May 1953, in preparation for the coronation coverage?

14. As the coronation approached, how were BBC television viewers made ready by Marguerite Patten?

15. Two officers from the London Metropolitan Police also appeared on a live broadcast prior to the big day. What advice did they give?

16. When Noel Coward was asked 'Who's that...?', in relation to a diminutive man seated in an open-top coach alongside a plus-size female dignitary from Polynesia, he famously replied, 'Her lunch'. It would become the most quoted line of the day. Who was the Polynesian dignitary?

17. Which dish was concocted specially for the occasion?

18. Why was a BBC journalist dismayed upon his return to Westminster Abbey at the end of the day, after all the congregation had left?

19. Which iconic young British actress, who would become a cornerstone of British *Carry On* comedy and, later, of soap opera, changed her surname in line with the Royal Family in 1952?

20. At the end of the afternoon, the Queen made how many balcony appearances with members of her family, cheered on by a euphoric crowd?

RUGBY
IN THE 1950s

1. Why did a game between France and Wales at Cardiff Arms Park in March 1950 begin with a minute's silence and the Last Post?

2. Which Welsh wing played for the Lions in 1950, but had previously won a silver medal in the 1948 Olympics Sprint Relay?

3. Which Welsh wonder boy became the first rugby player ever to have been flown out to play with the Lions as a last-minute replacement?

4. A record crowd of 48,500 fans gathered for a club match at Cardiff's Arms park in February 1951. Who were Cardiff playing?

5. Which nation won the Triple Crown for the ninth time in their history in March, 1952?

6. In February 1954, an international game was televised for the first time, from which UK rugby ground?

7. Why was a game played between a Scottish-Irish team and an English-Welsh team on 31st December, 1955, described as a 'Housewarming Game'?

8. Which Scottish full-back of the 1950s has been credited with having helped redefine the attacking role of the modern full-back?

9. Which Scottish wing held a First Class Honours degree in Mathematics and was a former long-jump champion?

10. Which Welsh centre was known affectionately as 'The Prince'?

11. Which English centre was described by the South African team in 1955 as the best centre they had ever seen, after he played against them with the Lions?

12. Which Scottish prop was known as 'The Abbot'?

13. Which England fly-half earned his first cap against Wales in 1956 and is the last English sportsman to have gained the status of double international, having also represented England in cricket in the 1960s?

14. In an article in *The Times* in 1957, the England team were lauded for winning all their Five Nations games that year. What phrase was used in the article for the first time to describe this achievement?

15. In a game between England and Ireland in Dublin in 1957, an England full-back used a new tactic in order to find touch from penalties, leading his team to a 6–0 victory. What was the tactic?

16. In October 1958, a once-lost grave was found in a cemetery in Menton, in the Alpes-Maritimes region of France. It was restored, bedecked with a Union Jack and a Tricolore and visited by the captain of the French rugby team, the French President and a brass band. Whose grave was it?

17. Who tracked the grave down?

18. In 1958, what change was made to the rules governing conversions?

19. Why did a capacity crowd observe a silent tribute at the start of the game between England and Ireland at Twickenham in February 1958?

20. What was notable about the Wales team jerseys at a game against England at Twickenham in 1958?

NAME THE

SITCOM

Name the British Television Sitcoms that featured the following cast

1. Valerie Singleton, Alexander Gauge, Donald Hewlett

2. Joan Shawlee, Patrick McGoohan, Michael Ward

3. Charles Hawtry, William Hartnell, Bernard Bresslaw, Dick Emery

4. Dick Bentley, Peter Sellers, Rosemary Miller, Herbert Mostyn

5. Avril Angers, Naomi Chance, Jack Melford

6. Jimmy James, Harry Secombe, Peter Sellers, Spike Milligan

7. Elsie Waters, Doris Waters, Hugh Paddick, Patsy Rowlands

8. Tony Hancock, Sid James, Bill Kerr, Kenneth Williams, Moira Lister (and later, Hattie Jacques)

9. Noel Dyson, Leslie Randall, Joan Reynolds, Harry Towb

10. David Kossof, Peggy Mount, Barbara Mitchell

11. Ben Lyon, Barbara Lyon, Richard Lyon

12. Arthur Askey, Richard Murdoch, Anthea Askey, Danny Ross

13. Evelyn Lane, Frank Lawton, Linda Gray, Peter Collingwood

14. Leslie Phillips, Joy Shelton, Anthea Holloway

15. Keith Crane, Michael Saunders, John Symonds, Meurig Wyn-Jones

16. Peter Sellers, Spike Milligan, Graham Stark, Kenneth Connor

17. Jack Allen, Ian Colin, Ronald Hines, Ian McNaughton, Henry McGee, Alan White

18. Billie Whitelaw, Diana King, Desmond Walter-Ellis

19. Bud Flanagan, Chesney Allen

20. Jimmy Edwards, Arthur Howard, Edwin Apps, John Stirling

DO YOU REMEMBER THE 1950s?

CELEBRITY

BIRTHS

AND DEATHS

1. Which Motown legend was born in Michigan in 1950?

2. Which British novelist, known for his dystopian vision of the future under a totalitarian regime, died in London in 1950?

3. Which Polish-Russian ballet dancer and choreographer, hailed as the finest ballet dancer of the century, died in London in 1950?

4. Which British drummer and singer was born in Chiswick, London in 1951?

5. Which African-American woman died of cancer in 1951, although cells taken from her without her knowledge live on in medicine in the form of the HeLa Cell line?

6. Which much-loved US comedian and actor was born in Chicago in 1951?

7. Which member of the British Royal Family died in February 1952?

8. Which Argentine state figure, hailed Argentina's 'Spiritual

Leader', died at the age of 33 in 1952?

9. Which US Country and Western star, known for hits such as 'Your Cheatin' Heart', died in West Virginia in 1953?

10. Which US astronomer, known for his pioneering work in extragalactic astronomy, died in San Marino in 1953?

11. Which US actress, talk show hostess and philanthropist was born in Mississippi in 1954?

12. Which ill-fated British mathematician and Bletchley Park codebreaker died in June 1954?

13. Which Mexican artist, known for her striking self-portraits, died in Mexico City in 1954?

14. Which actress, who was the second black woman in history to win an Academy Award, was born in New York in 1955?

15. Which German-born theoretical physicist, known for his groundbreaking work on the general theory of relativity, died in Princeton in 1955?

16. Which Texan model and actress, formerly married to a British rock legend, was born in 1956?

17. Which Academy Award-winning Hollywood actor was born in California in 1956?

18. Which groundbreaking US singer and actress was born into an Italian-American Roman Catholic family in Michigan in 1958?

19. Which US Hollywood actress, the daughter of two Hollywood greats of the golden era, was born in 1958?

20. Which British music and television producer, a household name on both sides of the Atlantic, was born in Lambeth, London in 1959?

Answers

The Year That Was – 1950

1. The Hydrogen Bomb
2. She gave birth to an illegitimate son, following her affair with film director Roberto Rossellini.
3. Communists
4. Cinderella
5. Clement Atlee
6. The removal of British troops from the Suez

Canal
7. They were all filmed in black-and-white, for the last time in the Oscars' history.
8. Eagle. Dan Dare, the comic's most enduring character, featured on the front cover of the inaugural issue.

9. Implemented a system of racial segregation across the country
10. Tollund Man, a pre-Romano bog-body
11. Ron L. Hubbard's Dianetics
12. The Archers
13. The Korean War
14. Uruguay beat Brazil, 2–1
15. Florence Chadwick, who

later became the first woman to swim the Channel in both directions
16. Paul Robeson
17. The containment of global Communism
18. Charles M. Schultz's Peanuts
19. Harvey
20. Shirley Temple

The Year That Was – 1951

1. The Archers
2. Nuclear testing at the Nevada Test Site
3. Presidents were to be limited to serving two terms in office
4. The King and I
5. Bette Davis and Anne Baxter

6. The Stone of Scone
7. The Soviet Union
8. Royal Festival Hall
9. Festival of Britain
10. The Goon Show
11. Showboat – Warfield sings 'Ol' Man River' in the film.
12. Oliver! Several close-ups

of Alec Guinness as Fagin were also cut for the US version.
13. J.D. Salinger's The Catcher in the Rye
14. The Miss World beauty pageant
15. Greece and Turkey
16. A blue sun caused by ash

from forest fires that had taken place four months earlier
17. Winston Churchill
18. The zebra crossing
19. Premier Supermarket – owned and operated by Express Dairies
20. The African Queen

The Year That Was – 1952

1. Sooty
2. TV detector vans
3. Because of the death of her father, King George VI
4. Compulsory identity cards
5. Japan
6. The B-52, a long-range jet-powered bomber

7. I Love Lucy
8. Southampton
9. Newcastle United
10. André Gide
11. Anne Frank
12. Trams
13. Helsinki

14. Lynmouth
15. Nothing: his experimental piece, 4'33", was entirely silent
16. Charlie Chaplin
17. News – not advertisements
18. He pulled his two brothers

from a house fire, sustaining extensive injuries and becoming the youngest ever recipient of the George Cross.
19. Republican, General Dwight D. Eisenhower
20. The Mousetrap

The Year That Was – 1953

1. Waiting for Godot
2. Physicians
3. An end to the rationing of sweets
4. Peter Pan
5. The structure of the DNA molecule
6. The scene of a number of

murders carried out by serial killer, John Christie
7. Queen Mary
8. James Bond, in Ian Fleming's first Bond novel, Casino Royale
9. Winston Churchill
10. Sir Edmund Hilary and

Sherpa Tenzing Norgay
11. Coronation of Queen Elizabeth II
12. LSD – used as part of an investigation into possible methods of mind control
13. The Quatermass Experiment

14. The Good Old Days
15. Gentlemen Prefer Blondes
16. Len Hutton
17. John F. Kennedy married Jacqueline Bouvier
18. UNICEF
19. Piltdown Man
20. Colour television sets

Answers

The Year That Was – 1954

1. Marilyn Monroe
2. Dylan Thomas – the play was Under Milk Wood
3. Smoking – a study in the late 1940s had been the first time the connection was made
4. Polio
5. Bikini Atoll
6. From Here to Eternity
7. Arturo Toscanini – the performance was his last, though he continued to record
8. Boeing 707
9. Diane Leather
10. J.R. Tolkein's Lord of the Rings
11. Alan Turing
12. UEFA (Union of European Football Associations)
13. A total eclipse of the sun
14. Meat
15. K2
16. Sports Illustrated
17. The Lone Ranger
18. The Suez Canal
19. Hancock's Half Hour
20. Burger King

The Year That Was – 1955

1. George Orwell's Animal Farm
2. The Big Freeze – snowdrifts as deep as 30 feet (9 metres) were recorded in some areas.
3. Elvis Presley
4. Bill Hayley and His Comets' Rock Around the Clock
5. The Associated Society of Locomotive Engineers and Firemen
6. Cyprus, which was a British colony until 1960
7. Anthony Eden
8. McDonald's
9. Albert Einstein
10. The Dam Busters
11. Horror comics
12. Ruth Ellis became the last woman to be hanged in the UK
13. Disneyland, the only Disney resort to have been designed by Walt Disney
14. Lady and the Tramp
15. The Guinness Book of Records
16. Kenneth Kendall and Richard Baker
17. Richard Nixon
18. Kim Philby
19. C. Northcote Parkinson, who later published a book entitled, Parkinson's Law
20. Richard III

The Year That Was – 1956

1. Italy
2. The Routemaster double-decker red bus
3. 'Heartbreak Hotel'
4. 'Que Sera, Sera (Whatever Will Be, Will Be)'
5. Karl Marx
6. Pakistan
7. Manchester United
8. Premium Bonds
9. Grace Kelly, who became Princess Grace of Monaco
10. Rocky Marciano
11. An anti-smoking campaign
12. John Osborne's Look Back in Anger
13. The Eurovision Song Contest
14. It was renamed, 'Second Class': since 1875 there had been only First and Third Class rail travel in the UK
15. Elvis Presley gyrated his hips suggestively while performing 'Hound Dog'.
16. The death penalty, but it would be defeated in the House of Lords on 10th July
17. Dean Martin and Jerry Lewis
18. Berni Inn Steakhouse
19. The Lancaster Bomber
20. PG Tips, featuring chimpanzees at a tea party

The Year That Was – 1957

1. It was the first electric watch
2. He became the first cricketer ever to have been dismissed for handling the ball during a Test
3. Elvis Presley – his provocative dance moves meant that he was only screened from the waist up
4. Harold Macmillan
5. The Frisbee
6. An hour between 6 and 7pm without any television broadcasts, to enable parents to put their children to bed
7. Dr Seuss' The Cat in the Hat
8. The harvesting of spaghetti from trees in Switzerland, reported by Richard Dimbleby
9. The Sky at Night with Patrick Moore
10. 42,000-pound hydrogen bomb
11. Stanley Matthews
12. John Lennon and Paul McCartney
13. Stirling Moss
14. 'We've never had it so good'
15. Andy Capp
16. The decriminalisation of homosexuality between consenting adults
17. Jodrell Bank
18. A dog named Laika
19. Wales
20. The queen delivered a Christmas message on television

Answers

The Year That Was – 1958

1. Sputnik 1
2. The plane carrying the Manchester FC team, known as 'Busby's Babes', crashed upon take-off at Munich airport
3. The Campaign for Nuclear Disarmament
4. The London Planetarium
5. Elvis Presley
6. The M1
7. Nikita Khrushchev
8. Family planning and contraception
9. Women
10. Gigi
11. The Duke of Edinburgh's Award
12. Ultrasound
13. Parking meters
14. Prince of Wales
15. NASA
16. Carry on Sergeant
17. 'Move It', by Cliff Richard
18. The Cod War
19. Blue Peter
20. Computers

The Year That Was – 1959

1. Fidel Castro
2. Charles de Gaulle
3. Motown Records
4. Sleeping Beauty
5. Cyprus
6. The Marx Brothers
7. Barbie
8. NASA's first seven military pilots selected to train for the space programme
9. Margot Fonteyn
10. Juke Box Jury
11. The Nun's Story
12. Klaus Fuchs
13. Postcodes
14. Barclays Bank
15. The Mini
16. Lunar 2, the Soviet un-manned spacecraft
17. The Xerox 914, the first photocopier
18. The Conservatives
19. Duty-free shopping
20. Ivor the Engine

Advertising Slogans of the Fifties

1. Wagon Wheels biscuits
2. 'Amplex', Amplex deodorant
3. Gibbs SR
4. 'Murray Mints'
5. PG Tips Tea
6. Hovis bread
7. Benson and Hedges cigarettes
8. 'Martell', Martell brandy
9. 'Oxo', Oxo stock cubes
10. Prestige cookware
11. 'Kellogg's way', Kellogg's Cornflakes
12. Potterton boilers
13. 'The Times', The Times newspaper
14. Sunblest bread
15. Omo laundry detergent
16. 'Fruit gums, mum', Rowntrees' Fruit Gums
17. 'Oldham', Oldham car battery
18. Fry's Turkish Delight
19. Meccano, construction kits
20. 'Heinz', Heinz salad cream

An Eclectic Mix of Human Advances

1. Corby, Northamptonshire
2. The Bic Biro
3. Jukebox, a highly colourful model with rotating displays of all 100 records
4. The Great Smog, caused by fog and heavy air pollution, prompting the Clean Air Act
5. Sir Edmund Hilary and Sherpa Tenzing Norgay made first ascent of Mount Everest
6. All black Americans were given the right to vote in all elections
7. 'Brown vs. the Board of Education' established that racial segregation of the US education system was unconstitutional
8. The 'Abominable Snowman', or yeti
9. The first sub-four-minute mile
10. Rosa Parks refused to vacate her seat in order to let a white passenger sit, in defiance of the segregation laws in place on the state's public transport. It sparked the Montgomery Bus Boycotts, led by Martin Luther King.
11. The first automatic kettle
12. Disneyland, the first Disney theme park and the only one designed by Walt Disney himself
13. Rocky Marciano
14. Sputnik, the first artificial Earth satellite
15. Laika became the first animal ever to have orbited the Earth, on board Sputnik 2.
16. He became the youngest Grandmaster of Chess
17. The Peace Symbol, originally designed for the Campaign for Nuclear Disarmament, incorporating the semaphore sign for 'N' and 'D'
18. Marie Curie
19. Antarctica
20. Javelin, with a revolving throw technique labelled the 'Spanish style'

Answers

Fifties Screen Idols: Audrey Hepburn

1. Brussels, Belgium, where she joined the Dutch Resistance during the Second World War
2. UNICEF
3. True: she was raised bilingually in English and Dutch and later learned to speak French, Spanish and Italian
4. Gigi
5. Roman Holiday
6. Roman Holiday
7. Mel Ferrer
8. Funny Face
9. Love in the Afternoon
10. A Nun's Story
11. The Diary of Anne Frank
12. Breakfast at Tiffany's
13. The Unforgiven
14. Holly Golightly
15. Cary Grant
16. 'Moon River'
17. Paris
18. By being alone: 'I have to be alone very often'
19. Her very large feet (size 10)
20. The little black Givenchy dress from Breakfast at Tiffany's

1950 to 1953 – Sporting Events

1. Brazil
2. American boxer, Ezzard Charles
3. Bobby Locke
4. The first event of the new World Drivers' Championship, won by Italian, Giuseppe Farina
5. Cambridge
6. Louise Brough Clapp of the US
7. Newcastle United
8. Randy Turpin
9. Ben Hogan
10. Juan Manuel Fangio
11. Ireland
12. Dick Savitt
13. Manchester United
14. A knock-out
15. Rocky Marciano
16. WWE
17. Blackpool
18. Jean Westwood and Lawrence Demmy
19. England
20. Fred Davis

British Television in the 1950s

1. Dixon of Dock Green
2. Watch With Mother
3. Panorama
4. Double Your Money
5. Emergency – Ward 10
6. Opportunity Knocks
7. Sunday Night at the London Palladium
8. Grandstand
9. Whirligig
10. Fabian of the Yard
11. The Buccaneers
12. The Woodentops
13. Oh Boy!
14. This Is Your Life
15. Pottery
16. Gibbs SR Toothpaste
17. A boxer spitting into a bucket in a live boxing match
18. Murray Mints – they performed with packets of Murray Mints which they threw at the audience
19. Strand cigarettes
20. It was donated to a charity nominated by the Lord Mayor of London

Classic Fifties Movies

1. Sunset Boulevard
2. Rio Grande
3. Quo Vadis
4. An American in Paris
5. Singin' in the Rain
6. A Streetcar Named Desire
7. Calamity Jane
8. How to Marry a Millionaire
9. Rear Window
10. White Christmas
11. Guys and Dolls
12. To Catch a Thief
13. High Society
14. The King and I
15. Old Yeller
16. Gunfight at the O.K. Corral
17. Dracula
18. The Fly
19. Some Like It Hot
20. Ben Hur

Answers

Comic Books of the 1950s

1. The Beano
2. The Dandy
3. Alf Tupper
4. Braddock
5. Eagle
6. Dan Dare, Pilot of the Future
7. Muffin the Mule
8. 'Horror' comics from the US, alleging a link between their presence in the UK and an increase in 'juvenile delinquency'
9. It was used as ballast in cargo ships, and consequently was originally only available on market stalls in the port cities, such as Liverpool, London and Belfast
10. The Children and Young Persons (Harmful Publications Act), banning violent and corrupting images in comics
11. Roger the Dodger
12. The Topper
13. Comic Cuts
14. Tiger
15. Roy of the Rovers
16. Hopalong Cassidy
17. The Beezer
18. The Comet
19. The Hotspur
20. Billy Bunter

Fifties Screen Idols – Elizabeth Taylor

1. She had both British and American citizenship
2. National Velvet
3. Her marriage to Conrad Hilton, Jr.
4. Quo Vadis
5. The Last Time I Saw Paris
6. James Dean, who died in a motorcar accident, just as the filming of Giant was coming to an end
7. Giant
8. Montgomery Clift. The two were close friends; Taylor rushed to the scene and pulled a tooth from Clift's throat to prevent him choking.
9. Giant
10. Cat on a Hot Tin Roof
11. BUtterfield 8
12. Suddenly, Last Summer
13. Seven: Conrad Hilton, Jr., Michael Wilding, Mike Todd, Eddie Fisher, Richard Burton, John Warner and Larry Fortensky. She married Burton twice.
14. 'Dogs and horses'
15. 'Big diamonds'
16. Mother Courage
17. Judaism
18. Suddenly, Last Summer
19. Butterfield 8
20. Cleopatra, 1963

Fashion in the Fifties

1. Christian Dior
2. Norman Hartnell
3. Hermes
4. The Baby Doll Dress, a trapeze-shaped dress with no waistline
5. Elvis Presley
6. Givenchy – who designed Hepburn's iconic little black dress for Breakfast At Tiffany's
7. Marks and Spencer
8. Givenchy
9. Crimpolene
10. Queen Elizabeth II and Elizabeth Taylor
11. The bullet bra
12. Creme Puff
13. Avon
14. The Italian Cut
15. The high ponytail
16. To produce pastel and coral shades of lipsticks and nail polish
17. Brothel Creepers
18. A poodle
19. Saddle shoes
20. The beehive

1954 to 56 – Sporting Events

1. Wolverhampton Wanderers
2. Switzerland
3. UEFA
4. Roger Bannister
5. Ed Sanders
6. Peter Thompson
7. Joe DiMaggio
8. Rocky Marciano
9. The US team won 8–4 over the British team
10. The LPGA Tour
11. Juan Miguel Fangio
12. Fred Davis
13. The title was shared between France and Wales
14. Louise Brough Clapp
15. Toni Sailer
16. The USSR
17. Rocky Marciano
18. Angela Buxton
19. Manchester United
20. New York Yankees

Answers

Fifties Fiction: Name the Novel

1. The Lord of the Rings
2. Catcher in the Rye
3. Charlotte's Web
4. Lord of the Flies
5. The Lion, The Witch and the Wardrobe
6. Fahrenheit 451
7. Lolita
8. The Old Man and the Sea
9. East of Eden
10. On The Road
11. Breakfast at Tiffany's
12. How the Grinch Stole Christmas!
13. Flowers for Algernon
14. Doctor Zhivago
15. The Talented Mr Ripley
16. I, Robot
17. The Borrowers
18. The Quiet American
19. A Bear Called Paddington
20. I Am Legend

Fifties Idols – Ella Fitzgerald

1. New York
2. Gershwin, she described it as 'a turning point' because she had previously limited herself solely to Jazz
3. The airline had refused to honour their First Class tickets
4. Marilyn Monroe, who promised the owner she'd take a front table every night
5. Pete Kelly's Blues
6. Gambling – they were released on bail in time to perform. Granz believed the arrest took place because the event was not segregated at his insistence.
7. Verve Records
8. Louis Armstrong, Ella and Louis, 1956 and Ella and Louis Again, 1957
9. Cole Porter
10. Porgy and Bess
11. Duke Ellington, who performed on half of the tracks for Ella Fitzgerald Sings the Duke Ellington Songbook in 1957
12. Denmark, where she began a relationship with a Danish man and bought a house in Copenhagen
13. Because Ellis was white: the network didn't want black and white musicians on screen together. Granz refused, so NBC smeared the camera lens with Vaseline to obscure Ellis.
14. 'Mack the Knife', from the 1960 album, Ella in Berlin
15. Frank Sinatra
16. '...the horns'
17. Billie Holiday
18. '...more singing'
19. John F. Kennedy
20. 'Can't Buy Me Love'

Fifties Hollywood Musicals: Name that Song

1. 'Luck Be A Lady', Guys and Dolls, 1955
2. 'Embraceable You', An American in Paris, 1951
3. 'Make 'Em Laugh', Singin in the Rain, 1952
4. 'Diamonds Are A Girl's Best Friend', Gentlemen Prefer Blondes, 1953
5. 'The Man That Got Away', A Star is Born, 1954
6. 'Something Wonderful', The King and I, 1956
7. 'True Love', High Society, 1956
8. 'Jailhouse Rock', Jailhouse Rock, 1957
9. 'Funny Face', Funny Face, 1957
10. 'Bless Yore Beautiful Hide', Seven Brides for Seven Brothers, 1954
11. 'That's Entertainment', The Band Wagon, 1953
12. 'Secret Love', Calamity Jane, 1953
13. 'Can't Help Lovin' Dat Man', Show Boat, 1951
14. 'Brush Up Your Shakespeare', Kiss Me Kate, 1953
15. 'I Remember it Well', Gigi, 1958
16. 'Some Enchanted Evening', South Pacific, 1958
17. 'Steam Heat', The Pajama Game , 1957
18. 'Oh, What a Beautiful Mornin'', Oklahoma, 1955
19. 'You Can't Get a Man With a Gun', Annie Get Your Gun, 1950
20. 'King Creole', King Creole, 1958

Fifties Sci-Fi Movie Classics

1. Destination Moon
2. The Day the Earth Stood Still
3. The Thing From Another World
4. When Worlds Collide
5. The Man From Planet X
6. The War of the Worlds
7. It Came From Outer Space
8. Invaders From Mars
9. Project Moonbase
10. 20,000 Leagues Under the Sea
11. Creature from the Black Lagoon
12. Them!
13. The Quatermass Xperiment – The Creeping Unknown
14. Forbidden Planet
15. Earth vs the Flying Saucers
16. Invasion of the Body Snatchers
17. The Incredible Shrinking Man
18. I Married a Monster From Outer Space
19. The Blob
20. Journey to the Centre of the Earth

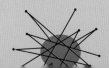

Answers

Fifties Stage Plays

1. The Cocktail Party, T.S. Eliot 1950
2. The Chairs, Eugene Ionesco, 1952
3. The Mousetrap, Agatha Christie, 1952
4. The Crucible, Arthur Miller, 1953
5. Waiting For Godot, Samuel Beckett, 1953
6. The Quare Fellow, Brendan Behan, 1954
7. Cat on a Hot Tin Roof, Tennessee Williams, 1955
8. A View From the Bridge, Arthur Miller, 1956
9. Long Day's Journey Into Night, Eugene O'Neill, 1956
10. Look Back in Anger, John Osborne, 1956
11. The Dumb Waiter, Harold Pinter, 1957
12. Endgame, Samuel Beckett, 1957
13. The Entertainer, John Osborne, 1957
14. Orpheus Descending, Tennessee Williams, 1957
15. The Potting Shed, Graham Greene, 1957
16. The Room, Harold Pinter, 1957
17. The Birthday Party, Harold Pinter, 1958
18. Krapp's Last Tape, Samuel Beckett, 1957
19. Suddenly, Last Summer, Tennessee Williams, 1958
20. The Unexpected Guest, Agatha Christie, 1958

Fifties Idols – Elvis Presley

1. Sun Records
2. 'That's All Right'
3. Louisiana Hayride
4. Roy Orbison
5. Rockabilly
6. Elvis Presley
7. The guitar
8. Elvis' grinding dance moves
9. Allen made him appear in Top Hat and Tails, singing 'Hound Dog' to a Bassett Hound
10. 'Hound Dog'/'Don't Be Cruel'
11. 'Love Me Tender'
12. Love Me Tender
13. Graceland
14. He dyed his hair black
15. Hollywood movies, where he said he 'lost my musical direction'
16. Frank Sinatra
17. '...herding sheep...'
18. The United States Army – Elvis was drafted for military service in March 1958
19. 14-year-old Priscilla Beaulieu, who became his wife 7 years later
20. '...think like men.'

Food in the Fifties

1. The Corona pop van; its motorized fleet pre-dated the war, but the company had reverted to horse and cart deliveries during the war years.
2. Spam
3. Jars of salmon paste
4. Heinz salad cream
5. Smiths Potato Crisps
6. Cockles, winkles and whelks
7. Weetabix and Shredded Wheat
8. Wimpy Bars
9. Bird's Eye Frozen fish fingers – the company sponsored freezers in local shops and freezer-less consumers bought the product on the day they planned to eat it.
10. Chinese restaurants became popular across the country; Billy Butlin added Chop Suey, served with chips
11. Bread and dripping
12. Liver, served either with bacon and onions or with dumplings
13. Olive oil
14. Pasta – available only in the form of macaroni, which was used exclusively for a milk-based pudding dish
15. Off the back of a horse and cart, decanted straight from the churns to the householder in pint jugs
16. Self-service, which began to creep in with the rise of the new supermarkets as the decade progressed
17. Sliced for you upon request, from whole sides of pigs
18. Weighed out by the pound upon request, from hundred-weight sacks
19. Cash was deposited in canisters and 'fired' by the assistant along ceiling wires to a cashier, who sat aloft. The customer's change and receipt would be fired back to them in the same way.
20. Broken biscuits

Name the Lady: Fifties Top 20 Hits

1. Doris Day
2. Lita Roza
3. Kitty Kallen
4. Vera Lynn
5. Connie Francis
6. Connie Francis
7. Rosemary Clooney
8. Kay Starr
9. Winifred Atwell
10. Ruby Murray
11. Alma Cogan
12. Kay Starr
13. Anne Shelton
14. Jane Morgan
15. Shirley Bassey
16. Muriel Smith
17. Eartha Kitt
18. Nancy Whiskey
19. Peggy Lee
20. Julie London

Answers

British Cars of the Fifties

1. Rover P4 75
2. Rolls Royce Phantom IV
3. Henri Matisse
4. Prince Ranier
5. Standard Vanguard
6. Winston Churchill
7. Ford Poplar
8. The Mercedes-Benz 300SL
9. Porsche 550 Spyder
10. Elvis Presley
11. Diana Dors
12. Richard Burton
13. Marilyn Monroe
14. The MG MGA
15. PA Velox and Cresta
16. Pablo Picasso
17. Brigitte Bardot
18. The Mini
19. Morris Minor
20. Sophia Loren

Inventive Firsts of the Fifties

1. Credit card
2. The first electric guitar, the Fender Esquire
3. Colour transmissions
4. Superglue
5. The thermonuclear, or hydrogen bomb
6. TV Dinner – a Thanksgiving meal in a compartmentalised foil tray
7. Transistor radio
8. The Electronic Music Synthesizer
9. Refrigerators ('Stratford Yellow' and 'Sherwood Green')
10. Automatic doors, which went into production in 1960
11. The first solar cell
12. Velcro
13. Lego
14. Scotchguard
15. The first video tape recorder
16. Alkaline batteries
17. Hula Hoop
18. The three-point car seat belt
19. The Barbie doll, sporting a black and white striped swimming costume
20. The first microchip

Fifties Screen Idols – James Dean

1. Pepsi
2. Stunt tester
3. Lee Strasberg at the Actors Studio
4. John Steinbeck, who disliked Dean's complex nature but felt it perfect for the role of Cal in East of Eden
5. Motor racing
6. Pier Angeli, who broke off the relationship to marry Vic Damone
7. Marlon Brando
8. Dying in a car, during a conversation about the danger of motor racing
9. Immortality
10. William Bast
11. Motor racing
12. Rebel Without a Cause
13. East of Eden
14. Giant
15. Giant
16. Rock Hudson, who thought Dean unprofessional. Hudson's wife later claimed Hudson was inconsolable and guilt-ridden upon learning of Dean's death.
17. Speeding, although in recent years it has been established that he could not have been driving over 55 miles per hour at the time of the crash
18. Its mangled wreckage toured the US with the National Safety Council to promote road safety
19. An Academy Award nomination: he remains the only actor to have been posthumously nominated for two Academy Awards for Best Actor, for East of Eden and Giant
20. J.R. Ewing – a man corrupted by oil wealth

Medical Firsts in the Fifties

1. The first organ transplant – she was given the kidney of a woman who had died from cirrhosis of the liver, without tissue typing or anti-infection drugs. It was rejected 10 months later.
2. The first antihistamines – particularly chlorpromazine, which made patients very sleepy
3. The first polio vaccine
4. Erythromycin
5. The cardiopulmonary bypass pump, the first heart-lung machine
6. Open-heart surgery
7. The discovery of the molecular structure of DNA
8. The first successful kidney transplant, carried out with identical twins
9. Cigarette smoking
10. The contraceptive pill
11. Tetracycline
12. Medical Ultrasound
13. The founding of the National Childbirth Trust. Grantly Dick-Read was an obstetrician who first advocated natural childbirth.
14. The human growth hormone
15. The first chemical synthesis of penicillin
16. Interferon
17. The laser
18. A coronary angiography
19. Internal pacemaker
20. Down syndrome

Answers

More Inventive Firsts of the Fifties

1. The telephone answering machine
2. Power steering
3. A built-in flash unit
4. The barcode
5. The first roll-on deodorant
6. The first sugar-free, diet drink
7. It was the first Technicolor, 3D movie with stereophonic sound
8. It was the first instant iced tea
9. The black box flight recorder
10. The Teflon-coated, non-stick pan
11. It was the first nuclear-powered submarine
12. Microwave ovens
13. It was the first remote control television
14. The first ski-doo, or snowmobile
15. The first hovercraft
16. The first liquid paper corrector fluid
17. The first computer hard disk
18. Bubble wrap
19. The computer modem
20. They were the first stereophonic recordings

Famous Film Quotes

1. Miss Casswell (Marilyn Monroe), All About Eve, 1950
2. Norma Desmond (Gloria Swanson), Sunset Boulevard, 1950
3. Jerry Mulligan (Gene Kelly), An American in Paris, 1951
4. George Eastman (Montgomery Clift), A Place in the Sun, 1951
5. Ned 'Scotty' Scott (Douglas Spencer), The Thing (From Another World), 1951
6. Martin Howe (Lon Cheney Jr.), High Noon, 1952
7. Karen Holmes (Deborah Kerr), From Here to Eternity, 1953
8. Lorelei Lee (Marilyn Monroe), Gentlemen Prefer Blondes, 1953
9. Joe Bradley (Gregory Peck), Roman Holiday, 1953
10. Terry Malloy (Marlon Brando), On the Waterfront, 1954
11. Vicki Lester (Judy Garland), A Star is Born, 1954
12. Jim Stark (James Dean), Rebel Without a Cause, 1955
13. The King of Siam (Yul Brynner), The King and I, 1956
14. Nickie Ferrante (Cary Grant), An Affair to Remember, 1957
15. Jo Stockton (Audrey Hepburn), Funny Face, 1957
16. Scott Carey (Grant Williams), The Incredible Shrinking Man, 1957
17. Maggie Pollitt (Elizabeth Taylor), Cat on a Hot Tin Roof, 1958
18. Scottie (James Stewart), Vertigo, 1958
19. Man at Prairie Crossing (Malcolm Atterby), North by Northwest, 1959
20. Jan Morrow (Doris Day), Pillow Talk (1959)

Fifties Screen Idols – Marilyn Monroe

1. Norma Jean Mortenson
2. Shelley Winters
3. To enable her to control a stutter she had had since childhood
4. Playboy
5. Gentlemen Prefer Blondes
6. Niagara
7. Joe DiMaggio
8. The Seven Year Itch
9. Arthur Miller
10. Bus Stop
11. Jean Harlow
12. Acting coach, Lee Strasberg (75%) and psychoanalyst, Marianne Kris (25%)
13. Books, many of which she annotated
14. Breakfast at Tiffany's
15. Ella Fitzgerald
16. A career
17. Face lifts
18. A President, with reference to John F. Kennedy
19. Sigmund Freud – Monroe underwent psychoanalysis in 1955 at the recommendation of acting coach, Lee Strasberg
20. President John F. Kennedy

Thirty Fifties Number One Hits

1. Guy Mitchell
2. The Stargazers
3. Johnnie Ray
4. David Whitfield
5. Frank Sinatra
6. Tony Bennett
7. Johnstone Brothers
8. Tennessee Ernie Ford
9. Dean Martin
10. Frankie Lymon and the Teenagers
11. Johnnie Ray
12. Guy Mitchell
13. Tab Hunter
14. Paul Anka
15. Lonnie Donegan
16. Buddy Holly and The Crickets
17. Perry Como
18. Conway Twitty
19. The Everly Brothers
20. Tommy Edwards
21. The Platters
22. Elvis Presley
23. Jerry Lee Richards
24. Elvis Presley
25. Buddy Holly
26. Bobby Darin
27. Craig Douglas
28. Cliff Richard
29. Emile Ford and the Checkmates
30. Adam Faith

Answers

Opportunity Knocks

1. BBC Light Programme
2. Spike Milligan
3. Alma Cogan
4. Tony Hancock
5. Radio Luxembourg
6. Hughie Green
7. Canadian
8. Double Your Money
9. In a Cessna aircraft, flown by Hughie Green, who had a pilot's licence
10. Engelbert Humperdinck (who used the name Gerry Dorsey until 1965)
11. Frankie Vaughan
12. The Clap-o-meter
13. 'Remember, the clap-o-meter is just for fun'
14. The home audience would write in on postcards
15. Manchester – the show was the last to have been aired at the ABC television studio in Didsbury, a former cinema
16. Frank Carson
17. Les Dawson – who didn't win, but lost out to the girlfriend of a West End nightclub owner.
18. 'I mean that most sincerely'
19. His right-wing political convictions; he believed the Harold Wilson Labour government were communists and advocated for the Duke of Edinburgh to step up as Prime Minister.
20. The Jam

Great Quotes from the Fifties

1. Joseph McCarthy, February 1950
2. Winston Churchill, Leader of the Opposition in a Commons debate on European union, June 1950
3. Aneurin Bevan, 1952
4. Anthony Eden, discussing the question of the UK forming a union with Europe, 1952
5. Presidential election campaign for Dwight D. Eisenhower, 1952
6. Svetlana Alliluyeva, Stalin's daughter, recounting her father's death, March 1953
7. Dwight D. Eisenhower, at the UN, December 1953
8. US Army Attorney General Joseph Welch, to Joseph McCarthy, June 1954
9. William Faulkner, 1956
10. Anthony Eden, discussing the Suez Crisis, August 1956
11. Dorothy Parker, 1956
12. Harold Macmillan, British Prime Minister, July 1957
13. Aneurin Bevan discussing unilateral nuclear disarmament at the Labour Party Conference, October 1957
14. Martin Luther king, Jr., 1957
15. Harold Macmillan, British Prime Minister, referring to the move towards independence among British colonies, July 1957
16. Ernest Hemingway, 1957
17. Truman Capote, 1957
18. Nikita Khrushchev, after visiting the US November 1959
19. Nikita Khrushchev, July 1959
20. Ernest Hemingway, 1958

Football in the Fifties

1. Brazil
2. They withdrew because of a FIFA ruling that their players could not play barefoot
3. Because of the unexpected win of the inexperienced, largely part-time US team over favourites, England
4. West Germany
5. Sweden
6. Hungary (The Mighty Magyars)
7. Pelé
8. All four home nations – England, Wales, Scotland and Northern Ireland - qualified
9. Wales got through to the quarter finals after a shock win against Hungary in the play-offs
10. John Charles, 'The Gentle Giant'
11. At the 1958 World Cup quarter final, Wales took on Brazil. The only goal of the match came from 17-year-old Pelé in the 66th minute.
12. Bill Shankly
13. Stanley Matthews
14. Stan Mortensen
15. Matt Busby
16. Wolverhampton Wanderers
17. The first European Cup tournament
18. Real Madrid
19. Bobby Charlton
20. The Munich Air Disaster, in which seven players lost their lives and a further two were too badly injured to ever return to football

Answers

Fifties Screen Idols – Marlon Brando

1. Realism – he was an early pioneer of Stanislavski's method acting
2. The lingerie department
3. A Streetcar Named Desire
4. Vivien Leigh
5. The director had falsely told Quinn Brando didn't rate his work, in order to create the tension needed for their on-screen personas
6. Mark Anthony in Julius Ceasar, co-starring John Gielgud. Gielgud was so impressed that he offered Brando a season at the Hammersmith Theatre, which Brando declined.
7. The Wild One
8. Triumph Thunderbird 6T
9. '...what to do'
10. He disapproved that director Elia Kazan had recently named a number of 'subversives' in the industry before the House Committee on Un-American Activities
11. Eve Marie Saint
12. 'I coulda been a contender': Kazan let Brando tenderly push away the gun his brother was holding to his head rather than deliver the entire speech at gunpoint, which Brando felt unrealistic.
13. He used it as a doorstop
14. Bette Davis
15. Guys and Dolls
16. Frank Sinatra – the two did not hit it off
17. '...plumber'
18. Sayonara
19. '...get out'
20. The Young Lions

School Days

1. Pen nibs fixed onto wooden holders and dipped in ink wells
2. Janet and John books
3. Ladybird books
4. Naptime
5. The nit nurses
6. Cod liver oil and malt extract
7. The liberty bodice
8. Elastic garters to keep their socks up
9. Free morning milk
10. Minced beef
11. 'Girls' and 'Boys': many schools segregated the school day
12. In cap and gowns
13. The 11+
14. Failure of the 11+ would mean heading to a Secondary Modern, rather than a Grammar School
15. They were generally outside
16. Shorts until the age of 11 years
17. The population 'bulge', or baby boom
18. Corporal punishment – the ruler, cane or strap
19. Rote-learning
20. The entire class rose to their feet

Sounds of the Fifties

1. 'Blueberry Hill'
2. Lloyd Price
3. Ten o'clock
4. True
5. 'Splish Splash'
6. The Shirelles
7. Alan Freed
8. 'Hound Dog'
9. Buddy Holly
10. B.B. King
11. Eddie Cochran
12. Wanda Jackson
13. Mississippi
14. 'Living Doll'
15. 'The Book of Love'
16. The Big Bopper
17. 'You Belong to Me'
18. Bo Diddley
19. 'Rock Around The Clock'
20. 'Maybelline'

Cricket in the Fifties

1. The West Indies
2. Lord Beginner
3. Len Hutton
4. They won the Ashes
5. Willie Watson
6. England
7. It was the only time in four decades (from the 1930s to the 1970s) that Australia were defeated at home
8. Fred Trueman
9. Tony Lock
10. Garfield Sobers
11. Khalid Hasan
12. Frank Tyson
13. He took all 10 wickets
14. The lowest run rates
15. Surrey
16. Bowler, Alec Bedser, Tony Lock and Jim Laker
17. Stuart Surridge
18. The women's team, White Heather
19. The International Women's Cricket Council
20. Australia

Answers

Famous Film Quotes

1. Margo Channing (Bette Davis), All About Eve, 1950
2. Elwood P. Dowd (James Stewart), Harvey, 1950
3. Klaatu (Michael Rennie), The Day The Earth Stood Still, 1951
4. Blanche DuBois (Vivien Leigh), A Streetcar Named Desire, 1951
5. Buttons, (James Stewart), The Greatest Show on Earth, 1952
6. Don Lockwood (Gene Kelly), Singin' in the Rain, 1952
7. Lorelei Lee (Marilyn Monroe), Gentlemen Prefer Blondes, 1953
8. Schatze Page (Lauren Bacall), How to Marry a Millionaire, 1953
9. Mildred (Peggy Maly) and Johnny (Marlon Brando), The Wild One, 1953
10. Stella (Thelma Ritter), Rear Window, 1954
11. Hubert Hawkins (Danny Kaye), The Court Jester, 1955
12. Marty Pilletti (Ernest Borgnine), Marty, 1955
13. Leslie Benedict (Elizabeth Taylor), Giant, 1956
14. Rameses (Yul Brynner), The Ten Commandments, 1956
15. Colonel Saito (Sessue Hayakawa), The Bridge on the River Kwai, 1957
16. Louise Carey (Randy Stewart), The Incredible Shrinking Man, 1957
17. Katie Coates (Dorothy McGuire), Old Yeller, 1957
18. Clara (Joanne Woodward), The Long, Hot Summer, 1958
19. Quintus Arrius (Jack Hawkins), Ben-Hur, 1959
20. Jerry (Jack Lemmon), Some Like it Hot, 1959

Teddy Boys and Girls

1. Savile Row, where post-war tailors attempted to revive Edwardian dress style for wealthy young Mayfair men and Oxbridge undergraduates.
2. East End gangs, often in their teens and often violent. They wore the long jackets, velvet collars and narrow trousers of the Edwardian style, claiming it for the working classes.
3. Joan Collins
4. Long Edwardian-style jackets with sleeves reaching to the fingertips
5. The murder of 17-year-old John Beckley in a gang clash
6. Judies
7. 'The Creep', a Dance Hall favourite with British Teddy Boys who were often known as 'Creepers'
8. Cameo brooches
9. A month's wages, though once the look took hold among South London gangs, it was soon abandoned by the Mayfair set, releasing affordable, second-hand Edwardian suits to London markets
10. Bill Haley and His Comets
11. The Maverick Gambler tie
12. Brighton
13. The Coolie
14. Ken Russell
15. Gender equality; the piece wondered did modern boys need to look more 'beautiful. . .romantic, colourful' to attract an independent woman
16. Long, Perspex-handled umbrellas
17. Blackboard Jungle ¬— the riot started when cinema staff attempted to stop the Teds dancing in the aisles to Bill Haley's 'Rock Around the Clock'
18. Tony Curtis
19. A popular Ted hairstyle, greased flat against the head at the sides and square cut at the nape of the neck
20. Ernest Ryman

The Olympics

1. Helsinki
2. The Soviet Union and the People's Republic of China
3. The People's Republic of China
4. Germany (The Federal Republic of Germany)
5. Oslo, Norway
6. New Zealand and Portugal
7. Melbourne, Australia
8. It was the first time the Olympics had been held in the Southern Hemisphere
9. Quarantine restrictions meant that horses couldn't enter Australia
10. The Suez Crisis and the Soviet crushing of the Hungarian Revolution
11. The Hungarian and Soviet teams were pitched against each other and it became very rough, sparking a near-riot. Hungary won 4–0.
12. All athletes assembled together, rather than marching as national teams behind their flags
13. The East and West German competitors were present as a single, unified team. This would be repeated until the 1968 Olympics.
14. He was the last Irish competitor to win a gold medal for any Olympic track event
15. He burned his arm
16. Cortina d'Ampezzo, Italy
17. They were within walking distance of each other
18. The Soviet Union
19. They were held outdoors for the last time
20. It was the first time the Winter Olympics had been aired to a multi-national television audience

Answers

The Space Race

1. A plan to launch satellites into space by 1958
2. To carry the Blue Streak Missile, providing the UK with a nuclear deterrent
3. The V2
4. He worried the Soviet Union could accuse the US of violating their sovereign airspace
5. The launch of Sputnik, a Soviet satellite, the first Earth satellite in history
6. The distinctive beep of the radio transmission made by Sputnik from space
7. The launch of the Vanguard test satellite, which exploded a metre into the air
8. The Van Allen radiation belt
9. Luna 1, launched by the Soviet Union
10. The far side of the Moon
11. Monkeys – Abel was a rhesus monkey and Miss Baker, a spider monkey. They were the first animals launched into space to be recovered alive.
12. President Eisenhower
13. Vanguard 2
14. Television images of the view of Earth from space – though they were blurred and didn't offer a full view. That didn't happen until the crew of Apollo 17 in 1972.
15. The UN Committee on the Peaceful Use of Outer Space
16. Googie architecture
17. Buck Rogers
18. Flash Gordon
19. A US intelligence-gathering satellite, used for photographic surveillance of the USSR
20. Dan Dare

Top Tracks by Fifties Bands

1. The Weavers
2. The Four Aces
3. Bill Haley and His Comets
4. The Chords
5. The Chordettes
6. The Platters
7. The McGuire Sisters
8. Buddy Holly and The Crickets
9. The Diamonds
10. The Everly Brothers
11. The Five Satins
12. Frankie Lymon and the Teenagers
13. The Del-Vikings
14. The Champs
15. The Flamingos
16. Jerry Butler and The Impressions
17. The Kingston Trio
18. The Drifters
19. The Coasters
20. The Dave Brubeck Quartet

1957 to 59 – Sporting Events

1. Stanley Matthews
2. Manchester United
3. Jackie Robinson
4. Patty Berg
5. England
6. Lew Hoad
7. Seven players died and two others, Johnny Berry and Jackie Blanchflower, were injured so badly they never played again.
8. Juan Miguel Fangio – he befriended his captors and came to sympathise with their cause. He was released unharmed after 29 hours – long enough to miss the Bastista Cuban Grand Prix.
9. Angela Mortimer
10. Cardiff
11. Pétanque
12. June Markham and Courtney Jones
13. Brazil, who beat the host-nation Sweden 5–2
14. Border, who scored 34 runs in the match
15. Gary Player
16. Betsy Rawls
17. Mike Hawthorn
18. France
19. Brazilian
20. Floyd Patterson

Toys and Games

1. Hornby Dublo (OO) model train sets
2. Cluedo
3. Enid Blyton's Noddy, from her book, Noddy's Adventures in Toyland
4. Dinky toys – the Guy Vans were part of their post-war 'Supertoys' range
5. Lesney's Matchbox series
6. Airfix kits
7. Scrabble
8. Lego, which launched its first 'Town Plan' kit in 1955
9. Play Doh
10. Yahtzee
11. Mettoy's Corgi cars
12. Scalextric – the first set cost £6 and demand outstripped the rate at which the kits could be produced
13. Paper dolls – used in the 1950s in the marketing of products such as Lyon's coffee and Swan soap
14. The Hula Hoop
15. Whip and Top
16. Cigarette cards, although as the decade progressed, this extended to other trade cards, including tea and biscuits
17. Bobbers
18. Hopscotch
19. British Bull Dog
20. Mr Potato Head

Answers

The Queen's Coronation

1. Westminster Abbey, London
2. She was the first ever to have lived to see her grandchild ascend to the throne
3. The orb, the sceptre, the rod of mercy and the royal ring of sapphire and rubies
4. Dr Geoffrey Fisher
5. 'God Save the Queen!'
6. '...be worthy of your trust'
7. Television audiences tuned into the BBC coverage: as there were only 2.7 million TV sets in the UK at the time, this meant an average of 7.5 people crowded around each set.
8. Film producer, Sir Alexander Korda, lent the Palace some of the coaches he used on film sets
9. Millionaire businessmen and members of the aristocracy offered their services and donned Buckingham Palace servants' uniforms for the day
10. Boiled sweets, which the Guards picked up on the tips of their swords
11. To the Commission's initial reticence to permit anything but the procession within the Abbey to be filmed, with cameras stationed strictly 'west of the organ screen'
12. No close-ups; the Queen was nervous of being televised
13. Rudimentary television transmitters, housed in outside-broadcast vans and manned by a crew of eight in a wooden hut with a chemical toilet
14. Snacks to be eaten in front of the television set: melon cocktails and salmon mousse
15. They advised on stepping up your home security so as to avoid being burgled while out of your home celebrating the coronation
16. The Queen of Tonga
17. Coronation Chicken
18. The seats from where the British aristocracy had watched the Coronation inside the Abbey were strewn with newspapers, whiskey bottles, sandwich wrappers and other detritus
19. Barbara Windsor (née Deeks)
20. Eight

Rugby in the 1950s

1. In memory of the 80 people, mostly Welsh rugby fans, who died in a plane crash upon their return from Dublin on 21st March, 1950
2. Ken Jones
3. Lewis Jones
4. Newport
5. Wales
6. Murrayfield – Scotland played New Zealand
7. It took place at Dublin's Lansdowne Road stadium, to mark the opening of an impressive new stand
8. Ken Scotland
9. Arthur Smith
10. Bleddyn Williams
11. Jeff Butterfield
12. Hugh McLeod
13. M.J.K. Smith, also known as Mike Smith
14. Grand Slam
15. He elected to use place-kicks
16. William Webb Ellis, the man credited with having first thought to pick up a ball and run with it during a ball game.
17. Ross McWhirter, founder of The Guinness Book of Records
18. The defence was no longer permitted to attempt to charge the kicker; instead the kicker would be allowed time to place the ball
19. To commemorate the victims of the Manchester United Munich air disaster
20. Their supplier had failed to deliver jerseys bearing the Prince of Wales emblem, so they had to play without

Name the Sitcom

1. The Adventures of Brigadier Wellington-Bull
2. The Adventures of Aggie
3. The Army Game
4. And So To Bentley
5. Dear Dotty
6. Don't Spare the Horses
7. Gert and Daisy
8. Hancock's Half Hour
9. Joan and Leslie
10. The Larkins
11. Life with the Lyons
12. Living It Up
13. My Husband and I
14. My Wife Jacqueline
15. Over to William
16. A Show Called Fred
17. Tell it to the Marines
18. Time Out For Peggy
19. Together Again
20. Whack-O!

Answers

Celebrity Births and Deaths in the 1950s

1. Stevie Wonder
2. George Orwell
3. Vaslav Nijinski
4. Phil Collins
5. Henrietta Lacks
6. Robin Williams
7. King George VI

8. Eva Peron
9. Hank Williams
10. Edwin Hubble
11. Oprah Winfrey
12. Alan Turing
13. Frieda Kahlo
14. Whoopi Goldberg

15. Albert Einstein
16. Jerry Hall
17. Tom Hanks
18. Madonna
19. Jamie Lee Curtis
20. Simon Cowell